'A' Level Maths is Really Hard

A level maths is seriously tricky — no question about that.

And as we sat around one afternoon, idly wondering what to do next to help the long-suffering youth out on the streets, we thought hey, let's ease the furrowed brows and do some A level maths.

So in putting this book together we've done everything we can to make things easier for you. For a start, we've tailor-made the book to your syllabus. We've scrutinised past paper questions, we've gone through the syllabus with a fine-toothed comb, we've found out everything you need to know and we've stayed up late, night after night, drinking large cups of cocoa and working out the best way to explain things.

We've done everything we can to help you understand what's going on. We've detailed the methods with as many helpful hints as you could possibly want — and we've given you two complete exam papers with worked examples, broken down and solved step-by-step. We've even tried to put some funny bits in to keep you awake — in short, we've put our "all" into this book.

We've done our bit — the rest is up to you.

What CGP's All About

The central aim of Coordination Group Publications is to produce top quality books that are carefully written, immaculately presented and astonishingly witty — whilst always making sure they exactly cover the syllabus for each subject.

And then we supply them to as many people as we possibly can, as <u>cheaply</u> as we possibly can.

Contents

SECTION FIVE — PROBABILITY AND STATISTICS

METHODS — PRACTICE EXAM 1

METHODS — PRACTICE EXAM 2

Published by Coordination Group Publications Ltd.

Contributors:
Charley Darbishire   BA (Hons)
Simon Little   BA (Hons)
Iain Nash   BSc
Andy Park   BSc (Hons)
Glenn Rogers   BSc (Hons)
Claire Thompson   BSc

ISBN: 1-84146-992-0

Groovy website: www.cgpbooks.co.uk

Jolly bits of clipart from CorelDRAW
With thanks to Ian Parkinson for the proof-reading

Printed by Elanders Hindson, Newcastle upon Tyne.

1000

Laws of Indices

You use the laws of indices all the time in maths — when you're integrating, differentiating and ...er.. well loads of other places. So take the time to get them sorted *now*.

> The Laws of Indices are the same thing as The Power Laws

Three mega-important Laws of Indices

You *must* know these three rules. I can't make it any clearer than that.

$$a^m \times a^n = a^{m+n}$$

If you multiply two numbers — you add their powers.

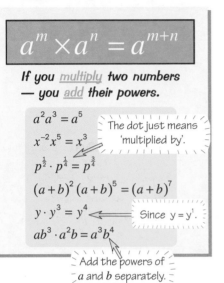

$$a^2 a^3 = a^5$$

$$x^{-2} x^5 = x^3$$

> The dot just means 'multiplied by'.

$$p^{\frac{1}{2}} \cdot p^{\frac{1}{4}} = p^{\frac{3}{4}}$$

$$(a+b)^2 (a+b)^5 = (a+b)^7$$

$$y \cdot y^3 = y^4$$

> Since $y = y^1$.

$$ab^3 \cdot a^2 b = a^3 b^4$$

> Add the powers of *a* and *b* separately.

$$\frac{a^m}{a^n} = a^{m-n}$$

If you divide two numbers — you subtract their powers.

$$\frac{x^5}{x^2} = x^3$$

$$\frac{x^{\frac{3}{4}}}{x} = x^{-\frac{1}{4}}$$

$$\frac{x^3 y^2}{xy^3} = x^2 y^{-1}$$

> Subtract the powers of x and y separately.

$$\left(a^m\right)^n = a^{mn}$$

If you have a power to the power of something else — multiply the powers together.

$$\left(x^2\right)^3 = x^6$$

$$\left\{(a+b)^3\right\}^4 = (a+b)^{12}$$

$$\left(ab^2\right)^4 = a^4 \left(b^2\right)^4 = a^4 b^8$$

> This power applies to both bits inside the brackets.

Other important stuff about Indices

You can't get very far without knowing this sort of stuff. Learn it — you'll definitely be able to use it.

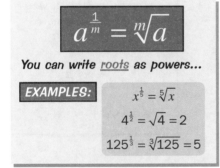

$$a^{\frac{1}{m}} = \sqrt[m]{a}$$

You can write roots as powers...

EXAMPLES:

$$x^{\frac{1}{5}} = \sqrt[5]{x}$$

$$4^{\frac{1}{2}} = \sqrt{4} = 2$$

$$125^{\frac{1}{3}} = \sqrt[3]{125} = 5$$

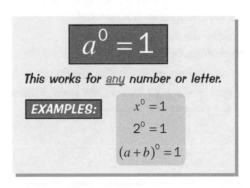

$$a^{\frac{m}{n}} = \sqrt[n]{a^m} = \left(\sqrt[n]{a}\right)^m$$

A power that's a fraction like this is the root of a power — or the power of a root.

EXAMPLES:

$$9^{\frac{3}{2}} = \left(9^{\frac{1}{2}}\right)^3 = \left(\sqrt{9}\right)^3 = 3^3 = 27$$

$$16^{\frac{3}{4}} = \left(16^{\frac{1}{4}}\right)^3 = \left(\sqrt[4]{16}\right)^3 = 2^3 = 8$$

> It's often easier to work out the root first, then raise it to the power.

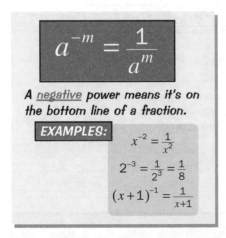

$$a^{-m} = \frac{1}{a^m}$$

A negative power means it's on the bottom line of a fraction.

EXAMPLES:

$$x^{-2} = \frac{1}{x^2}$$

$$2^{-3} = \frac{1}{2^3} = \frac{1}{8}$$

$$(x+1)^{-1} = \frac{1}{x+1}$$

$$a^0 = 1$$

This works for any number or letter.

EXAMPLES:

$$x^0 = 1$$

$$2^0 = 1$$

$$(a+b)^0 = 1$$

Indices, indices — de fish all live indices...

[B]lah, blah, *important*. Blah, blah, *learn* these. Blah, blah, *use* them all the time. Mmm, that's about all that needs to be said.

Surds

A surd is a number like $\sqrt{2}$, $\sqrt[3]{12}$ or $5\sqrt{3}$ — one that's written with the $\sqrt{}$ sign. They're important because you can give _exact_ answers where you'd otherwise have to round to a certain number of decimal places.

Surds are sometimes the only way to give an Exact Answer

Put $\sqrt{2}$ into a calculator and you'll get something like 1.414213562...
But square 1.414213562 and you get 1.999999999.

And no matter how many decimal places you use, you'll never get _exactly_ 2.
The only way to write the exact, spot on value is to use surds.

So unless the question asks for an answer to a certain
number of decimal places — leave your answer as a surd.

There are basically Three Rules _for using_ Surds

There are three _rules_ you'll need to know to be able to use surds properly. Check out the 'Rules of Surds' box below.

EXAMPLES: (i) Simplify $\sqrt{12}$ and $\sqrt{\dfrac{3}{16}}$.   (ii) Show that $\dfrac{9}{\sqrt{3}} = 3\sqrt{3}$.   (iii) Find $\left(2\sqrt{5} + 3\sqrt{6}\right)^2$.

(i) _Simplifying_ surds means making the number in the $\sqrt{}$ sign _smaller_, or getting rid of a _fraction_ in the $\sqrt{}$ sign.

$$\sqrt{12} = \sqrt{4 \times 3} = \sqrt{4} \times \sqrt{3} = 2\sqrt{3}$$

$$\sqrt{\frac{3}{16}} = \frac{\sqrt{3}}{\sqrt{16}} = \frac{\sqrt{3}}{4}$$

Using $\sqrt{\dfrac{a}{b}} = \dfrac{\sqrt{a}}{\sqrt{b}}$.

Using $\sqrt{ab} = \sqrt{a}\sqrt{b}$.

(ii) For questions like these, you have to write a number (here, it's 3) as $3 = \left(\sqrt{3}\right)^2 = \sqrt{3} \times \sqrt{3}$.

$$\frac{9}{\sqrt{3}} = \frac{3 \times 3}{\sqrt{3}} = \frac{3 \times \sqrt{3} \times \sqrt{3}}{\sqrt{3}} = 3\sqrt{3}$$

Cancelling $\sqrt{3}$ from the top and bottom lines.

Rules of Surds

There's not really very much to remember.

$$\sqrt{ab} = \sqrt{a}\,\sqrt{b}$$

$$\sqrt{\frac{a}{b}} = \frac{\sqrt{a}}{\sqrt{b}}$$

$$a = \left(\sqrt{a}\right)^2 = \sqrt{a}\,\sqrt{a}$$

(iii) Multiply surds very _carefully_ — it's easy to make a silly mistake.

$$\left(2\sqrt{5} + 3\sqrt{6}\right)^2 = \left(2\sqrt{5} + 3\sqrt{6}\right)\left(2\sqrt{5} + 3\sqrt{6}\right)$$

$$= \left(2\sqrt{5}\right)^2 + 2 \times \left(2\sqrt{5}\right) \times \left(3\sqrt{6}\right) + \left(3\sqrt{6}\right)^2$$

$$= \left(2^2 \times \sqrt{5}^2\right) + \left(2 \times 2 \times 3 \times \sqrt{5} \times \sqrt{6}\right) + \left(3^2 \times \sqrt{6}^2\right)$$

$$= 20 + 12\sqrt{30} + 54$$

$$= 74 + 12\sqrt{30}$$

$= 4 \times 5 = 20$

$= 12\sqrt{5}\sqrt{6} = 12\sqrt{30}$

$= 9 \times 6 = 54$

Remove surds from the bottom of fractions by Rationalising the Denominator

Surds are pretty darn complicated.
So they're the last thing you want
at the bottom of a fraction.

But have no fear — _Rationalise the Denominator_...

Yup, you heard... (it means getting rid of the surds
from the bottom of a fraction).

EXAMPLE: Rationalise the denominator of $\dfrac{1}{1+\sqrt{2}}$

Multiply the top and bottom by the denominator (but change the sign in front of the surd).

$$\frac{1}{1+\sqrt{2}} \times \frac{1-\sqrt{2}}{1-\sqrt{2}}$$

$$\frac{1-\sqrt{2}}{\left(1+\sqrt{2}\right)\left(1-\sqrt{2}\right)} = \frac{1-\sqrt{2}}{1^2 + \sqrt{2} - \sqrt{2} - \sqrt{2}^2}$$

This works because:
$(a+b)(a-b) = a^2 - b^2$

$$\frac{1-\sqrt{2}}{1-2} = \frac{1-\sqrt{2}}{-1} = -1 + \sqrt{2}$$

Surely the pun is mightier than the surd...

There's not much to surds really — but they cause a load of hassle. Think of them as just ways to save you the bother of getting your calculator out and pressing buttons — then you might grow to know and love them. The box of rules in the middle is the vital stuff. Learn them till you can write them down without thinking — then get loads of practice with them.

Algebraic Fractions

No one likes fractions. But just like Mondays, you can't put them off forever. Face those fears. Here goes...

The first thing you've got to know about fractions:

You can just add the stuff on the top lines because the bottom lines are all the same.

$$\frac{a}{x} + \frac{b}{x} + \frac{c}{x} \equiv \frac{a+b+c}{x}$$

x is called a common denominator — a fancy way of saying 'the bottom line of all the fractions is x'.

This is the <u>identity</u> sign: ≡ It means "is exactly the same as". You use ≡ instead of = to say that whatever's on the left is always exactly the same as the thing on the right, no matter what the values of the variables.

Add fractions by putting them over a Common Denominator...

Finding a common denominator just means 'rewriting some fractions so all their bottom lines are the same'.

EXAMPLE: Simplify $\dfrac{1}{2x} - \dfrac{1}{3x} + \dfrac{1}{5x}$

You need to rewrite these so that all the bottom lines are equal. What you want is something that all these bottom lines divide into.

PUT IT OVER A COMMON DENOMINATOR

30 is the lowest number that 2, 3, and 5 go into. So the common denominator is 30x.

$$\frac{15}{30x} - \frac{10}{30x} + \frac{6}{30x}$$

Always check that these divide out to give what you started with.

$$= \frac{15 - 10 + 6}{30x} = \frac{11}{30x}$$

...even horrible looking ones

Yep, finding a common denominator even works for those fraction nasties — like these:

EXAMPLE: Simplify $\dfrac{2y}{x(x+3)} + \dfrac{1}{y^2(x+3)} - \dfrac{x}{y}$

FIND THE COMMON DENOMINATOR

Take all the individual 'bits' from the bottom lines and multiply them together. Only use each bit once unless something on the bottom line is squared.

The individual 'bits' here are x, (x+3) and y...

$$xy^2(x+3)$$

...but you need to use y^2 because there's a y^2 in the second fraction's denominator.

PUT EACH FRACTION OVER THE COMMON DENOMINATOR

Make the denominator of each fraction into the common denominator.

$$\frac{y^2 \times 2y}{y^2 x(x+3)} + \frac{x \times 1}{xy^2(x+3)} - \frac{xy(x+3) \times x}{xy(x+3)y}$$

Multiply the top and bottom lines of each fraction by whatever makes the bottom line the same as the common denominator.

COMBINE INTO ONE FRACTION

Once everything's over the common denominator — you can just add the top lines together.

As always — if you see a minus sign, look out for possible problems.

$$= \frac{2y^3 + x - x^2 y(x+3)}{xy^2(x+3)}$$

All the bottom lines are the same — so you can just add the top lines.

$$= \frac{2y^3 + x - x^3 y - 3x^2 y}{xy^2(x+3)}$$

All you need to do now is tidy up the top.

Not the nicest of answers. But it <u>is</u> the answer, so it'll have to do.

Well put me over a common denominator and pickle my walrus...

Adding fractions — turning lots of fractions into one fraction. Sounds pretty good to me, since it means you don't have to write as much. Better do it carefully, though — otherwise you can watch those marks disappear into thin air.

Manipulating Brackets

In this horrific nightmare that is A-level maths, you need to manipulate and simplify expressions all the time.

Remove **brackets** by Multiplying **them out**

Here are the basic types you have to deal with. You'll have seen them before. But there's no harm in reminding you, eh?

Multiply Your Brackets Here — we do all shapes and sizes

SINGLE BRACKETS

$$a(b+c+d) = ab+ac+ad$$

SQUARED BRACKETS

$$(a+b)^2 = (a+b)(a+b) = a^2 + 2ab + b^2$$

Use the middle stage until you're comfortable with it. Just _never_ make this _mistake_: $(a+b)^2 = a^2 + b^2$

DOUBLE BRACKETS

$$(a+b)(c+d) = ac+ad+bc+bd$$

LONG BRACKETS

Write it out again with _each term_ from one bracket separately multiplied by the _other bracket_.

$$(x+y+z)(a+b+c+d)$$
$$= x(a+b+c+d) + y(a+b+c+d) + z(a+b+c+d)$$

Then _multiply out each_ of these _brackets_, one at a time.

Spot those Common Factors

Common factors need to be hunted down and taken outside the brackets. They are a danger to your exam mark. A bit which is in _each term_ of an expression is a _common factor_.

SPOT THOSE COMMON FACTORS $2x^3z + 4x^2yz + 14x^2y^2z$ ← Look for any bits that are in each term.

Numbers: There's a common factor of 2 here because 2 divides into 2, 4 and 14.

Variables: There's at least an x^2 in each term and there's a z in each term.

So there's a __common factor of $2x^2z$__ in this expression.

AND TAKE THEM OUTSIDE A BRACKET

If you spot a common factor you can "_take it out_":

Write the common factor outside a bracket... $2x^2z(x + 2y + 7y^2)$

and put what's left of each term inside the bracket:

Afterwards, always _multiply back out_ to check you did it right:

CHECK BY MULTIPLYING OUT AGAIN

$$2x^2z(x + 2y + 7y^2) = 2x^3z + 4x^2yz + 14x^2y^2z$$

EXAMPLE: Simplify... $(x+1)(x-2) + (x+1)^2 - x(x+1)$

There's an **(x+1)** factor in each term, so we can take this out as a _common factor_ (hurrah).

The terms inside the big bracket are the old terms with an (x+1) removed. $(x+1)\{(x-2) + (x+1) - x\}$

At this point you should check that this multiplies out to give the original expression. (You can just do this in your head, if you trust it.)

Then simplify the big bracket's innards:

$$(x+1)(\cancel{x} - 2 + x + 1 - \cancel{x})$$
$$= (x+1)(x-1)$$
$$= x^2 - 1$$

Get this answer by multiplying out the two brackets (or by using the "difference of two squares").

Go forth and multiply out brackets...

OK, so this is obvious, but I'll say it anyway — if you've got 3 or more brackets together, multiply them out _2 at a time_. Then you'll be turning a really hard problem into two easy ones. And if you're ever asked to simplify an expression, always _look for common factors first_ — it's the quickest way to simplify something. Got that? Simple i'n'it...

Factorising a Quadratic

Factorising a quadratic usually means putting it into two brackets — and is useful if you're trying to draw a graph of a quadratic or solve a quadratic equation. It's pretty easy if $a = 1$ (in $ax^2 + bx + c$ form), but can be a real pain otherwise.

$$x^2 - x - 12 = (x - 4)(x + 3)$$

Factorising's not so bad when $a = 1$

EXAMPLE: Solve $x^2 - 8 = 2x$ by factorising.

A

PUT INTO $ax^2 + bx + c = 0$ FORM

$x^2 - 2x - 8 = 0$ ⟵ So $a = 1$, $b = -2$, $c = -8$.

Write down the two brackets with x's in: $x^2 - 2x - 8 = (x \quad)(x \quad)$

B

FIND THE TWO NUMBERS

Find two numbers that _multiply_ together to make 'c' but which also _add_ or _subtract_ to give 'b' (you can ignore any minus signs for now).

This is the value for 'b' you're after — so this is the right combination: 2 and 4.

1 and 8 multiply to give 8 — and add / subtract to give 9 and 7.

2 and 4 multiply to give 8 — and add / subtract to give 6 and 2.

C

FIND THE SIGNS

Now all you have to do is put in the _plus_ or _minus_ signs.

If c is negative, then the signs must be different.

$x^2 - 2x - 8 = (x \quad 4)(x \quad 2)$

$x^2 - 2x - 8 = (x + 2)(x - 4)$

It must be +2 and −4 because $2 \times (-4) = -8$ and $2 + (-4) = 2 - 4 = -2$

You could do these two steps in one. You'd be looking for two numbers that multiply together to make −8 and add to make −2.

E.g. $-1 \times 8 = -8$
$1 \times -8 = -8$
$-2 \times 4 = -8$
$2 \times -4 = -8$

D

SOLVE THE EQUATION

All you've done so far is to factorise the equation — you've still got to solve it.

Don't forget this last step. The factors aren't the answer.

$(x + 2)(x - 4) = 0$

$\Rightarrow x + 2 = 0$ or $x - 4 = 0$

$\Rightarrow x = -2$ or $x = 4$

Factorising Quadratics

A) Rearrange the equation into the standard $ax^2 + bx + c$ form.

B) Write down the two brackets:
$(x \quad)(x \quad)$

C) Find two numbers that multiply to give 'c' and add / subtract to give 'b' (ignoring signs).

D) Put the numbers in the brackets and choose their signs.

Another Example...

This equation is already in the standard format — you can write down the brackets straight away.

EXAMPLE: Solve $x^2 + 4x - 21 = 0$ by factorising.

$x^2 + 4x - 21 = (x \quad)(x \quad)$

This is the value of 'b' you're after — 3 and 7 are the right numbers.

1 and 21 multiply to give 21 — and add / subtract to give 22 and 20.

3 and 7 multiply to give 21 — and add / subtract to give 10 and 4.

$x^2 + 4x - 21 = (x + 7)(x - 3)$

And solving the equation to find x gives... $\Rightarrow x = -7$ or $x = 3$

Scitardauq Gnisirotcaf — you should know it backwards...

Factorising quadratics — this is _very_ basic stuff. You've really got to be comfortable with it. If you're even slightly rusty, you need to practise it until it's second nature. Remember why you're doing it — you don't factorise simply for the pleasure it gives you — it's so you can _solve_ quadratic equations. Well, that's the theory anyway...

Factorising a Quadratic

It's not over yet...

Factorising a quadratic when $a \neq 1$

These can be a real pain. The basic method's the same as on the previous page — but it can be a bit more awkward.

EXAMPLE: Factorise $3x^2 + 4x - 15$

A **WRITE DOWN TWO BRACKETS**

As before, write down two brackets — but instead of just having x in each, you need two things that will multiply to give $3x^2$.

It's got to be $3x$ and x here.

$$3x^2 + 4x - 15 = \left(3x \qquad\right)\left(x \qquad\right)$$

B **THE FIDDLY BIT**

You need to find two numbers that <u>multiply together</u> to make 15 — but which will give you $4x$ when you multiply them by x and $3x$ and then add / subtract them.

$\left(3x \quad 1\right)\left(x \quad 15\right) \Rightarrow x$ and $45x$ which then add or subtract to give **46x** and **44x**.

$\left(3x \quad 15\right)\left(x \quad 1\right) \Rightarrow 15x$ and $3x$ which then add or subtract to give **18x** and **12x**.

$\left(3x \quad 3\right)\left(x \quad 5\right) \Rightarrow 3x$ and $15x$ which then add or subtract to give **18x** and **12x**.

$\left(3x \quad 5\right)\left(x \quad 3\right) \Rightarrow 5x$ and $9x$ which then add or subtract to give **14x** and **4x**.

This is the value you're after — so this is the right combination.

C **ADD THE SIGNS**

You know the brackets must be like these... $\Rightarrow \left(3x \quad 5\right)\left(x \quad 3\right) = 3x^2 + 4x - 15$

So all you have to do is put in the plus or minus signs.

You've only got two choices — if you're unsure, just multiply them out to see which one's right.

$$(3x + 5)(x - 3) = 3x^2 - 4x - 15$$

or...

$$(3x - 5)(x + 3) = 3x^2 + 4x - 15 \Longleftarrow \text{So it's this one.}$$

'c' is negative — that means the signs in the brackets are different.

Sometimes it's best just to Cheat and use the Formula

Here's two final points to bear in mind:

1) It <u>won't</u> always factorise.

2) Sometimes factorising is so <u>messy</u> that it's easier to just use the quadratic formula...

So if the question doesn't tell you to factorise, don't assume it will factorise.
And if it's something like this thing below, don't bother trying to factorise it...

EXAMPLE: Solve $6x^2 + 87x - 144 = 0$

This <u>will</u> actually factorise, but there's 2 possible bracket forms to try.

$\left(6x \qquad\right)\left(x \qquad\right)$ or $\left(3x \qquad\right)\left(2x \qquad\right)$ And for each of these, there's 8 possible ways of making 144 to try.

And you can quote me on that... err, well maybe not...

"He who can properly do quadratic equations is considered a god."
Plato

"Quadratic equations are the music of reason."
James J Sylvester

Section One Revision Questions

So that was the first section. And let's face it, it wasn't that bad. But it's all really important _basic stuff_ that you need to be very comfortable with — otherwise A-level maths will just become a never-ending misery. Anyway, before you get stuck into Section Two, test yourself with these questions. Go on. If you thought this section was a doddle, you should be able to fly through them... (They're also very helpful if you're having trouble sleeping.)

1) Simplify these: (Hint: Remember when to add or subtract the powers.)

a) $x^3.x^5$ b) $a^7.a^8$ c) $\dfrac{x^8}{x^2}$ d) $\left(a^2\right)^4$ e) $\left(xy^2\right).\left(x^3yz\right)$ f) $\dfrac{a^2b^4c^6}{a^3b^2c}$

2) Work out the following:

a) $16^{\frac{1}{2}}$ b) $8^{\frac{1}{3}}$ c) $16^{\frac{3}{4}}$ d) x^0 e) $49^{-\frac{1}{2}}$ Fractional powers... mmm...

3) Find exact answers to these equations:

a) $x^2 - 5 = 0$ b) $(x+2)^2 - 3 = 0$

4) Simplify:

a) $\sqrt{28}$ b) $\sqrt{\dfrac{5}{36}}$ c) $\sqrt{18}$ d) $\sqrt{\dfrac{9}{16}}$

5) Show that a) $\dfrac{8}{\sqrt{2}} = 4\sqrt{2}$, and b) $\dfrac{\sqrt{2}}{2} = \dfrac{1}{\sqrt{2}}$

6) Find $\left(6\sqrt{3} + 2\sqrt{7}\right)^2$

7) Rationalise the denominators of these numbers: a) $\dfrac{3}{1+\sqrt{7}}$, b) $\dfrac{2}{\sqrt{3}-1}$, c) $\dfrac{7\sqrt{3}}{2+\sqrt{5}}$

8) Put the following expressions over a common denominator:

a) $\dfrac{2x}{3} + \dfrac{y}{12} + \dfrac{x}{5}$ b) $\dfrac{5}{xy^2} - \dfrac{2}{x^2y}$ c) $\dfrac{1}{x} + \dfrac{x}{x+y} + \dfrac{y}{x-y}$

9) Simplify these expressions:

a) $\dfrac{2a}{b} - \dfrac{a}{2b}$ b) $\dfrac{2p}{p+q} + \dfrac{2q}{p-q}$ c) "A bird in the hand is worth two in the bush"

10) What symbol should be used instead of the equals sign in identities?

11) Remove the brackets and simplify the following expressions:

a) $(a+b)(a-b)$ b) $(a+b)(a+b)$ c) $35xy + 25y(5y+7x) - 100y^2$

d) $x(x-2)(1+y) - (x^2-2x)(y+2)$ e) $(x+3y+2)(3x+y+7)$

12) Take out the common factors from the following expressions:

a) $2x^2 + 4x + 6x^3$ b) $6x^2yz + 2y^2z - 3yz^2$ c) $16y + 8yx + 56x$ d) $x(x-2) + 3(2-x)$

13) Factorise the following expressions. While you're doing this, sing a jolly song to show how much you enjoy it.

a) $x^2 + 2x + 1$,   b) $x^2 - 13x + 30$,   c) $x^2 - 4$,   d) $3 + 2x - x^2$

e) $2x^2 - 7x - 4$,   f) $5x^2 + 7x - 6$.

14) Factorise and solve the following equations. And sing verse two of your jolly song.

a) $x^2 - 3x + 2 = 0$,   b) $x^2 + x - 12 = 0$,   c) $2 + x - x^2 = 0$,   d) $x^2 + x - 16 = x$

e) $3x^2 - 15x - 14 = 4x$,   f) $4x^2 - 1 = 0$,   g) $6x^2 - 11x + 9 = 2x^2 - x + 3$.

Did someone say Powers?

The Quadratic Formula

Unlike factorising, the quadratic formula always works... no ifs, no buts, no butts, no nothing...

The Quadratic Formula — a reason to be cheerful, but careful...

If you want to solve a quadratic equation $ax^2 + bx + c = 0$, then the answers are given by this formula:

$$x = \frac{-b \pm \sqrt{b^2 - 4ac}}{2a}$$

The formula's a <u>godsend</u> — but use the power wisely...

> If any of the coefficients (i.e. if a, b or c) in your quadratic equation are negative — be <u>especially</u> careful.

> Always take things nice and <u>slowly</u> — don't try to rush it.

> It's a good idea to write down what a, b and c are <u>before</u> you start plugging them into the formula.

> There are a couple of minus signs in the formula — which can catch you out if you're not paying <u>attention</u>.

I shall teach you the ways of the Formula

EXAMPLE: Solve the quadratic equation $3x^2 - 4x = 8$ to **2 d.p.**

> The mention of decimal places is a <u>big</u> clue that you should use the formula.

REARRANGE THE EQUATION

Get the equation in the standard $ax^2 + bx + c = 0$ form.

$3x^2 - 4x = 8$

$3x^2 - 4x - 8 = 0$

FIND a, b AND c

Write down the coefficients a, b and c — making sure you don't forget minus signs.

$3x^2 - 4x - 8 = 0$

$a = 3 \qquad b = -4 \qquad c = -8$

STICK THEM IN THE FORMULA

Very carefully, plug these numbers into the formula. It's best to write down each stage as you do it.

$$x = \frac{-b \pm \sqrt{b^2 - 4ac}}{2a}$$

$$= \frac{-(-4) \pm \sqrt{(-4)^2 - 4 \times 3 \times (-8)}}{2 \times 3}$$

> Until you've finished, keep <u>at least</u> one or two more decimal places than you'll eventually need.

$$= \frac{4 \pm \sqrt{16 + 96}}{6}$$

$$= \frac{4 \pm \sqrt{112}}{6}$$

> Don't round numbers up or down unless you have to — use surds where possible. (See page 2.)

> The $\pm$ sign means that you have two different expressions for x — which you get by replacing the $\pm$ with + and –.

$$= \frac{4 \pm 10.5830}{6}$$

> Round to 2 d.p. (or whatever you've been asked to round to) but <u>only</u> when you've finished the calculation.

$$x = 2.43 \ or - 1.10$$

Using this magic formula, I shall take over the world... ha ha ha...

Okay, maybe it's not <u>quite</u> that good... but it's really important. So learn it properly — which means spending enough time until you can just say it out loud the whole way through, with no hesitations. Or perhaps you could try singing it as loud as you can to the tune of your favourite cheesy song. Sha-la-la-la-la-la-la-ha... La-di-da... Sha-la-la-la-la-la-la-ha... La-di-da... Sha-la-la-la-la-la-la-ha...

The Quadratic Formula

By using part of the quadratic formula, you can quickly tell if a quadratic equation has two solutions, one solution, or no solutions at all. Tell me more, I hear you cry...

How Many Roots? Check the b² – 4ac bit...

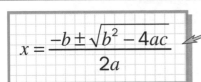

$$x = \frac{-b \pm \sqrt{b^2 - 4ac}}{2a}$$

When you try to find the roots of a quadratic function, this bit in the square-root sign ($b^2 - 4ac$) can be positive, zero, or negative. It's _this_ that tells you if a quadratic function has two roots, one root, or no roots.

The $b^2 - 4ac$ bit is called the _discriminant_.

Because — if the discriminant is positive, the formula will give you two different values — when you add or subtract the $\sqrt{b^2 - 4ac}$ bit.

But if it's zero, you'll only get one value, since adding or subtracting zero doesn't make any difference.

And if it's negative, you don't get any (real) values because you can't take the square root of a negative number.

Well, not in Methods. In later modules, you can actually take the square root of negative numbers and get 'imaginary' numbers.

It's good to be able to picture what this means:

A root is just when y = 0, so it's where the graph touches or crosses the x-axis.

$b^2 - 4ac > 0$	$b^2 - 4ac = 0$	$b^2 - 4ac < 0$
Two roots	One root	No roots

So the graph crosses the x-axis twice and these are the roots:

The graph just touches the x-axis from above (or from below if the x^2 coefficient is negative).

The graph doesn't touch the x-axis at all.

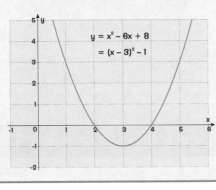

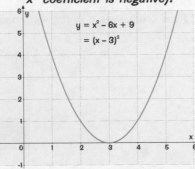

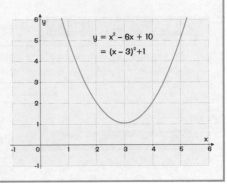

EXAMPLE: Find the range of values of k for which: a) f(x)=0 has 2 distinct roots, b) f(x)=0 has 1 root, c) f(x) has no real roots, where $f(x) = 3x^2 + 2x + k$.

First of all, work out what the discriminant is: $b^2 - 4ac = 2^2 - 4 \times 3 \times k$
$$= 4 - 12k$$

These calculations are exactly the same. You don't need to do them if you've done a) because the _only difference_ is the equality symbol.

a) _Two distinct roots_ means:
$$b^2 - 4ac > 0 \Rightarrow 4 - 12k > 0$$
$$\Rightarrow 4 > 12k$$
$$\Rightarrow k < \tfrac{1}{3}$$

b) _One root_ means:
$$b^2 - 4ac = 0 \Rightarrow 4 - 12k = 0$$
$$\Rightarrow 4 = 12k$$
$$\Rightarrow k = \tfrac{1}{3}$$

c) _No roots_ means:
$$b^2 - 4ac < 0 \Rightarrow 4 - 12k < 0$$
$$\Rightarrow 4 < 12k$$
$$\Rightarrow k > \tfrac{1}{3}$$

ha ha ha ha haaaaaa... ha ha ha... ha ha ha ... ha ha ha........

So for questions about "how many roots", think discriminant — i.e. b² – 4ac. And don't get the inequality signs (> and <) the wrong way round. It's obvious, if you think about it. Remember: >0 means two roots, 0 means one root, and <0 means no roots.

<u>Completing the Square</u>

Completing the Square is a handy little trick that you should <u>definitely</u> know how to use.
It can be a bit fiddly — but it gives you <u>loads</u> of information about a quadratic really quickly.

<u>Take any old quadratic and put it in a Special Form</u>

Completing the square can be really confusing. For starters, what does "Completing the Square" <u>mean</u>?
<u>What</u> is the square? <u>Why</u> does it need completing? Well, there is <u>some</u> logic to it:

1) The <u>square</u> is something like this: $(x+\text{something})^2$ It's basically the factorised equation (with the factors both the same), but there's something missing...

2) ...So you need to '<u>complete</u>' it by adding a number to the square to make it equal to the original equation. $(x+\text{something})^2 + d$

You'll start with something like this...   ...sort the x-coefficients...   ...and you'll end up with something like this

$$2x^2 + 8x - 5$$ → $$2(x+2)^2 + ?$$ → $$2(x+2)^2 - 13$$

Lovely!

<u>Make completing the square a bit Easier</u>

There are only a few stages to completing the square — if you can't be bothered trying to understand it,
just <u>learn how to do it</u>. But I reckon it's worth spending a bit more time to get your head round it <u>properly</u>.

Take Out A Factor Of 'a'

— take a factor of a out of the x^2 and x terms.

$f(x) = 2x^2 + 3x - 5$ ←This is in the form $ax^2 + bx + c$

This '2' is an 'a'.

$f(x) = 2\left(x^2 + \frac{3}{2}x\right) - 5$ ←Check that the bracket multiplies out to what you had before.

This is $\frac{b}{a}$

Rewrite The Bracket — rewrite the bracket as one bracket squared.

The number in the brackets is <u>always</u> $\frac{b}{2a}$ half the old number in front of the x.

$f(x) = 2\left(x + \frac{3}{4}\right)^2 + d$ ← d is a number you have to find to make the new form equal to the old one.

Don't forget the 'squared' sign.

Complete The Square — find d.

To do this, <u>make the old and new equations equal each other</u>...

$2\left(x+\frac{3}{4}\right)^2 + d = 2x^2 + 3x - 5$

...and you can find d.

$2x^2 + 3x + \frac{9}{8} + d = 2x^2 + 3x - 5$

The x^2 and x bits are the same on both sides so they can disappear.

$\frac{9}{8} + d = -5$

$\Rightarrow d = -\frac{49}{8}$

<u>Completing the Square</u>

A) <u>THE BIT IN THE BRACKETS IS ALWAYS</u> — $a\left(x + \frac{b}{2a}\right)^2$

B) <u>CALL THE NUMBER AT THE END d</u> — $a\left(x + \frac{b}{2a}\right)^2 + d$

C) <u>MAKE THE TWO FORMS EQUAL</u> — $ax^2 + bx + c = a\left(x + \frac{b}{2a}\right)^2 + d$

So The Answer Is:

$f(x) = 2x^2 + 3x - 5 = 2\left(x + \frac{3}{4}\right)^2 - \frac{49}{8}$

<u>Complete your square — it'd be root not to...</u>

Remember — you're basically trying to write the expression as one bracket squared, but it doesn't quite work. So you have to add a number (d) to make it work. It's a bit confusing at first, but once you've learnt it, you won't forget it in a hurry.

Completing the Square

Once you've completed the square, you can very quickly say <u>loads</u> about a quadratic function.
And it all relies on the fact that a squared number can <u>never</u> be less than zero... <u>ever</u>.

Completing the square can sometimes be Useful

This is a quadratic written as a completed square. As it's a quadratic
function and the coefficient of x^2 is positive, it's a u-shaped graph.

This is a square — it can never be negative.
The smallest it can be is 0.

$$f(x) = 3x^2 - 6x - 7 = 3(x-1)^2 - 10$$

FIND THE MINIMUM — make the bit in the brackets equal to zero.

When the squared bit is zero, f(x)
reaches its minimum value.
This means the graph reaches its
lowest point.

$$f(x) = 3(x-1)^2 - 10$$

This number here
is the minimum.

$$f(1) = 3(1-1)^2 - 10$$

f(1) means using
x = 1 in the function.

$$f(1) = 3(0)^2 - 10 = -10$$

So the minimum
is –10, when x = 1.

B

WHERE DOES f(x) CROSS THE x-AXIS?

Make the completed square
function equal zero.

Solve it to find where f(x)
crosses the x-axis.

$$3(x-1)^2 - 10 = 0$$

$$\Rightarrow (x-1)^2 = \frac{10}{3}$$

da-de-dah ...
rearranging again.

$$\Rightarrow x - 1 = \pm\sqrt{\frac{10}{3}}$$

$$\Rightarrow x = 1 \pm \sqrt{\frac{10}{3}}$$

So f(x) crosses the x-axis when... $x = 2.83 \ or -0.83$

These notes are all about graphs with
<u>positive</u> coefficients in front of the x^2.
But if the coefficient is negative, then
the graph is flipped <u>upside-down</u> (n-
shaped, not u-shaped). That means you
find the maximum, <u>not</u> the minimum.

With this information, you
can easily sketch the graph...

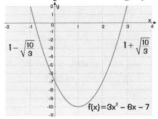

Some functions don't have Real Roots

By completing the square, you can also quickly tell if the graph of a quadratic function ever crosses the x-axis.
It'll only cross the x-axis if the function changes sign (i.e. goes from positive to negative or vice versa).
Take this function...

FIND THE ROOTS $f(x) = x^2 + 4x + 7$

This number's positive.

$$f(x) = (x+2)^2 + 3$$

The smallest this bit can
be is zero (at x = –2).

So f(x) is always bigger
than zero — in fact
never less than three.

If the coefficient of x^2 is negative, you
can do the same sort of thing to check
whether f(x) ever becomes positive.

This means that:

a) f(x) can <u>never</u> be negative.
b) The graph of f(x) <u>never</u> crosses the x-axis.

d don't forget — two wrongs don't make a root...

You'll be pleased to know that that's the end of me trying to tell you how to do something you probably really don't want to do.
Now you can push it to one side and run off to roll around in a bed of nettles... much more fun.

Sketching Quadratic Graphs

If a question doesn't seem to make sense, or you can't see how to go about solving a problem, try drawing a __graph__. It sometimes helps if you can actually __see__ what the problem is, rather than just reading about it.

Sketch the graphs of the following quadratic functions:

① $y = 2x^2 - 4x + 3$

② $y = 8 - 2x - x^2$

Quadratic graphs are _Always_ u-shaped or n-shaped

The first thing you need to know is whether the graph's going to be u-shaped or n-shaped (upside down). To decide, look at the _coefficient of x^2_.

$y = 2x^2 - 4x + 3$

The coefficient of x^2 here is _positive_... ...so the graph's u-shaped. **+ve**

$y = 8 - 2x - x^2$

The coefficient of x^2 here is _negative_... ...so the graph's upside down (n-shaped). **−ve**

Now find the places where the graph crosses the _axes_ (both the y-axis and the x-axis).

(i) Put x = 0 to find where it meets the _y-axis_.

$y = 2x^2 - 4x + 3$

$y = (2 \times 0^2) - (4 \times 0) + 3$ **so** $y = 3$

That's where it crosses the y axis.

(ii) Solve y = 0 to find where it meets the _x-axis_.

$2x^2 - 4x + 3 = 0$

$b^2 - 4ac = -8 < 0$

You could use the formula. But first check $b^2 - 4ac$ to see if y = 0 has any roots.

So it has no solutions, and doesn't cross the x-axis.

(i) Put x = 0.

$y = 8 - 2x - x^2$

$y = 8 - (2 \times 0) - 0^2$ **so** $y = 8$

(ii) Solve y = 0.

$8 - 2x - x^2 = 0$

$\Rightarrow (2 - x)(x + 4) = 0$

$\Rightarrow x = 2 \text{ or } x = -4$

This equation factorises easily...

Finally, find the _minimum_ or _maximum_.

Since $y = 2(x - 1)^2 + 1$

By _completing the square_.

the minimum value is $y = 1$, which occurs at $x = 1$.

The minimum or maximum of the graph is always at $x = \dfrac{-b}{2a}$.

The maximum value is _halfway_ between the roots — the graph's symmetrical

The maximum value is at $x = -1$

So the maximum is $y = 8 - (2 \times -1) - (-1)^2$

i.e. the graph has a maximum at the point (−1,9).

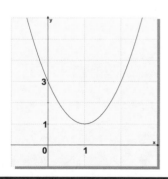

Sketching Quadratic Graphs

A) **UP OR DOWN** — decide which direction the curve points in.

B) **AXES** — find where the curve crosses them.

C) **MAX / MIN** — find the turning point.

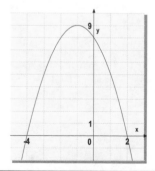

Van Gogh, Monet — all the greats started by sketching graphs...

So there's three steps here to learn. Simple enough. You can do the third step (finding the max/min point) by either a) completing the square, which is covered a bit later, or b) using the fact that the graph's symmetrical — so once you've found the points where it crosses the x-axis, the point halfway between them will be the max/min. It's all laughs here...

'Almost' Quadratic Equations

Sometimes you'll be asked to solve equations that look really difficult, like the ones on this page. But with a bit of rearrangement and fiddling you can get them to look just like an ordinary quadratic you can solve.

Some Nasty-looking equations are just Quadratics

$$x^4 + 3x^2 + 6 = 0$$

Arrrgh. How on earth are you supposed to solve something like that? Well the answer is... with great difficulty — that's if you don't spot that you can turn it into quadratic form like this:

$$(x^2)^2 + 3(x^2) + 6 = 0$$

It still looks weird. But, if those x^2's were y's:

$$y^2 + 3y + 6 = 0$$

Now it's a just a simple quadratic that you could solve in your sleep — or the exam, which would probably be more useful.

$$2\sin^2 t - 3\sin t - 2 = 0$$

...it looks hard

$$2(\sin t)^2 - 3(\sin t) - 2 = 0$$

...still looks hard

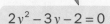

$$2y^2 - 3y - 2 = 0$$

...looks easy.

Just make a Substitution to Simplify

EXAMPLE: $2x^6 - 11x^3 + 5 = 0$

1 **SPOT THAT IT'S A QUADRATIC**

Put it in the form: a(something)² + b(same thing) + (number) = 0.

$$2(x^3)^2 - 11(x^3) + 5 = 0$$

Now substitute y for x^3 to make it like a normal quadratic.

2 **SUBSTITUTE**

let $x^3 = y \Rightarrow 2y^2 - 11y + 5 = 0$

And solve this quadratic to find the values of y.

3 **SOLVE IT**

$$2y^2 - 11y + 5 = 0$$
$$(2y - 1)(y - 5) = 0$$
$$y = \tfrac{1}{2}, \text{ or } 5$$

Now you've got the values of y, you can get the values of x.

4 **FIND THE ORIGINAL UNKNOWN x**

$y = \tfrac{1}{2}, \text{ or } 5$ but... $y = x^3$ ← This comes from stage 2.

Which means... $x^3 = \tfrac{1}{2}, \text{ or } 5$

$$x = \sqrt[3]{\tfrac{1}{2}}, \text{ or } \sqrt[3]{5}$$

So the answer is... $x = 0.79, \text{ or } 1.71$

Disguised Quadratics

1) Put the equation in the **FORM** :

   a(something)²+b(same thing)+(number)=0

2) **SUBSTITUTE** y for the something in the brackets to get a normal-looking quadratic.

3) **SOLVE** the quadratic in the usual way — i.e. by factorising or using the quadratic formula.

4) Stick your answers in the substitution equation to get the values for the **ORIGINAL** unknown.

Almost quadratics... almost interesting... almost worthwhile... almost...

Quadratics with delusions of grandeur. Whatever next. "Nuff about quadratics!" I hear you cry. Well it's all over now, so you can relax... ahhh ...just relax... ...mmm... ...nice.... ...ah... Hang on. You're only halfway through the section.

The Fantastic Factor Theorem

The factor theorem is fantastic — no doubt about it. It can really help you factorise cubics. But not only that, at this week's special CGP price of only £27.49*, thanks to its twin rotating blades, it allows a closer factorisation than ever before. So for smoother, closer, and faster factorising, choose the CGP Fantastic Factor Theorem every time.

Feel the power of the Factor Theorem

The Factor Theorem's dead useful, and is certainly going to be of use come the exam. And don't forget it's fantastic.

> ### THE FANTASTIC FACTOR THEOREM:
>
> If f(x) is a polynomial, and f(a) = 0, then (x – a) is a factor of f(x).
>
> In other words: If you know the roots, you also know the factors — and vice versa.

EXAMPLE: Show that $(x+1)$ is a factor of $f(x) = x^3 + 4x^2 - 7x - 10$

The question's giving you a _big_ hint here. If you show that f(–1) = 0, then the factor theorem says that (x + 1) is a factor.

$$f(x) = x^3 + 4x^2 - 7x - 10$$

$$f(-1) = -1 + 4 + 7 - 10 = 0$$

So, by the factor theorem, (x+1) is a factor of f(x).

See pages 5-6 for more on factorising.

You can use the Factor Theorem when $a \neq 1$

You might be asked to show that (ax – b) (i.e. something with a number in front of the x) is a factor of a polynomial. But don't start panicking just yet — you can still use the factor theorem.

EXAMPLE: Show that $(2x-1)$ is a factor of $f(x) = 2x^2 - 9x + 4$

Notice that 2x – 1 = 0 when x = ½. Plug this value of x into f(x).

$$f(x) = 2x^2 - 9x + 4$$

$$f\left(\tfrac{1}{2}\right) = 2\left(\tfrac{1}{2}\right)^2 - \left(9 \times \tfrac{1}{2}\right) + 4$$

$$f\left(\tfrac{1}{2}\right) = \tfrac{1}{2} - \tfrac{9}{2} + 4 = 0$$

So by the factor theorem, (x – ½) is a factor.
And if that's a factor, then 2 (x – ½) = (2x – 1) is also a factor†.

†**Explanation of a tricky bit...**
If you _multiply_ one factor by a number, you've got to _divide_ the other factor by the _same number_.

e.g.
$$f(x) = \left(x - \tfrac{1}{2}\right)(p)$$
$$f(x) = (2x-1)\left(\tfrac{1}{2}p\right)$$

e.g.
$$8 \times 6 = 48$$
$$(8 \times 3)(6 \div 3) = 48$$
$$(24)(2) = 48$$

(x–1) is a Factor if the coefficients add up to 0

This is a useful thing to remember.
It works for all polynomials — no exceptions.
It could save a fair whack of time in the exam.

EXAMPLE: Factorise the polynomial $f(x) = 6x^2 - 7x + 1$

The coefficients (6, –7 and 1) add up to 0. That means f(1) = 0. And that applies to _any polynomial_ at all... always.

So by the factor theorem, if f (1) = 0, (x – 1) is a factor. Easy.

Just factorise it like an easy quadratic to get this:

$$f(x) = 6x^2 - 7x + 1 = (6x-1)(x-1)$$

* Plus Postage and Packaging, at £28.49. Allow at least 28 months for delivery.

You've lost that Factor Theorem, whoah, yeah that Factor Theorem...

You know, I had NO idea how great a factor I could get. Not until I tried CGP's Fantastic Factor Theorem.
I used to have problems with factorisation when dating, and in my general life. But now I've put all that behind me.
Now I've got the confidence to talk about factors wherever I go. I can really experience the joy of factorising.
And it's all thanks to CGP's Fantastic Factor Theorem: Try it today — it changed my life, and it could change yours too.

Factorising Cubics

Factorising a quadratic function is okay — but you might also be asked to factorise a cubic (something with x^3 in it). And that takes a bit more time — there are more steps, so there are more chances to make mistakes.

Factorising **a cubic given** One Factor

$$f(x) = 2x^3 + x^2 - 8x - 4$$

Factorising a cubic means exactly what it meant with a quadratic — putting brackets in.
When they ask you to factorise a cubic equation, they'll usually tell you one of the factors.

EXAMPLE: Given that $(x + 2)$ is a factor of $f(x) = 2x^3 + x^2 - 8x - 4$, express $f(x)$ as the product of three linear factors.

① The first step is to find a quadratic factor. So write down the factor you know, along with another set of brackets.

$$(x+2)(\qquad\qquad) = 2x^3 + x^2 - 8x - 4$$

Put the x^2 bit in this new set of brackets.
These have to _multiply together_ to give you this.

$$(x+2)(2x^2\qquad\quad) = 2x^3 + x^2 - 8x - 4$$

② Find the number for the second set of brackets.
These have to _multiply together_ to give you this.

$$(x+2)(2x^2\qquad -2) = 2x^3 + x^2 - 8x - 4$$

③ These multiplied give you $-2x$, but there's $-8x$ in $f(x)$ — so you need an 'extra' $-6x$. And that's what this $-3x$ is for.

$$(x+2)(2x^2 - 3x - 2) = 2x^3 + x^2 - 8x - 4$$

You only need $-3x$ because it's going to be multiplied by 2, which makes $-6x$.

If you wanted to solve a cubic, you'd do it _exactly_ the same way — put it in the form $ax^3 + bx^2 + cx + d = 0$ and factorise.

Factorising Cubics

1) Find a factor, (if you need to) by finding $f(0)$, $f(\pm 1)$, $f(\pm 2)$,.... until you find $f(k) = 0$. Then $(x - k)$ is a factor.

2) Put in the x^2 term.

3) Put in the constant.

4) Put in the x term by comparing the number of x's on both sides.

5) Check there are the same number of x^2's on both sides.

6) Factorise the quadratic you've found — if that's possible.

④ Before you go any further, check that there are the same number of x^2's on _both_ sides.

$4x^2$ from here...

$$(x+2)(2x^2 - 3x - 2) = 2x^3 + x^2 - 8x - 4$$

...and $-3x^2$ from here...   ...add together to give this x^2.

If this is okay, factorise the quadratic into two linear factors.

$$(2x^2 - 3x - 2) = (2x + 1)(x - 2)$$

And so... $2x^3 + x^2 - 8x - 4 = (x+2)(2x+1)(x-2)$

Factorising **a cubic given** No Factors

If they don't give you the first factor, you have to find it _yourself_. But it's okay — they'll give you an easy one. The best way to find a factor is to _guess_ — use trial and error.

FIND f(1) If the answer is zero, you know $(x - 1)$ is a factor.
If the answer isn't zero, find $f(-1)$. If that's zero, then $(x + 1)$ is a factor.

If that doesn't work, keep trying small numbers (find $f(2)$, $f(-2)$, $f(3)$, $f(-3)$ and so on) until you find a number that gives you _zero_ when you put it in the _cubic_. Call that number k.

$(x - k)$ is a _factor of the cubic_ (from the Factor Theorem).

I love the smell of fresh factorised cubics in the morning...

Factorising cubics is exactly the same as learning to unicycle... It's impossible at first. But when you finally manage it, it's really easy from then onwards and you'll never forget it. Probably. To tell the truth, I can't unicycle at all. So don't believe a word I say.

Section Two Revision Questions

Mmmm, well, quadratic equations — not exactly designed to make you fall out of your chair through laughing so hard, are they? But (and that's a huge 'but') they'll get you plenty of marks come that fine morning when you march confidently into the exam hall — if you know what you're doing. And what better way to make sure you know what you're doing than to practise. So here we go then, on the thrill-seeker's ride of a lifetime — the CGP quadratic equation revision section...

1) Solve the following equations using the quadratic formula.

    a) $x^2 - 3x + 2 = 0$,   b) $x^2 + x - 12 = 0$,

    c) $2 + x - x^2 = 0$,   d) $x^2 + x - 16 = x$

    e) $3x^2 - 15x - 14 = 4x$,   f) $4x^2 - 1 = 0$,

    g) $6x^2 - 11x + 9 = 2x^2 - x + 3$.

2) Rewrite these quadratics by completing the square.
Then state their maximum or minimum value and the value of x where this occurs.

    a) $x^2 - 4x - 3$,   b) $3 - 3x - x^2$,

    c) $2x^2 - 4x + 11$,   d) $4x^2 - 28x + 48$.

3) How many roots do these quadratics have? Sketch their graphs.

    a) $x^2 - 2x - 3 = 0$,   b) $x^2 - 6x + 9 = 0$,   c) $2x^2 + 4x + 3 = 0$.

4) Solve these quadratic equations to two decimal places.

    a) $3x^2 - 7x + 3 = 0$,   b) $2x^2 - 6x - 2 = 0$,   c) $x^2 + 4x + 6 = 12$.

5) Find all the solutions to the following equations. (Quite tricky, these — especially that last one.)

    a) $x^4 - 17x^2 + 16 = 0$,   b) $x^{\frac{4}{3}} - 5x^{\frac{2}{3}} + 4 = 0$.

6) If the quadratic equation $x^2 + kx + 4 = 0$ has two roots, what are the possible values of k?

7) Show that $(x + 2)$ is a factor of $x^3 + 5x^2 + 2x - 8$.

8) a) Show that $(3x - 1)$ is a factor of $3x^3 + 23x^2 + 37x - 15$.

    b) Factorise $x^3 - x^2 - 4x + 4$ into three factors.

OK, I think that's enough. Go and make yourself a cup of tea. Treat yourself to a chocolate biscuit.

Here is a new way to enjoy Pelican biscuits:

Bite a small piece off two opposite corners of a Pelican.
Immerse one corner in coffee, and suck coffee up through the Pelican,
like a straw. You will need to suck quite hard to start with.
After a few seconds you will notice the biscuit part of the Pelican start to
lose structural integrity. At this point, cram it into your mouth, where it
will collapse into a mass of hot molten chocolate, biscuit and coffee.

Great stuff.

Simultaneous Equations — Elimination

Solving simultaneous equations means finding the answers to two equations _at the same time_ — i.e. finding values for x and y for which both equations are true. And it's one of those things that you'll have to do _again and again_ — so it's definitely worth practising them until you feel _really confident_.

① $3x + 5y = -4$
② $-2x + 3y = 9$

This is how simultaneous equations are usually shown. It's a good idea to label them as equation ① and equation ② — so you know which one you're working with.

But they'll look different sometimes, maybe like this. Make sure you rearrange them as 'ax + by = c'.

$4 + 5y = -3x$
$-2x = 9 - 3y$

rearrange as
ax + by = c

$3x + 5y = -4$
$-2x + 3y = 9$

Solving them by _Elimination_

Elimination is a lovely method. It's really quick when you get the hang of it — you'll be doing virtually all of it in your head.

EXAMPLE
① $3x + 5y = -4$
② $-2x + 3y = 9$

To get the x's to match, you need to multiply the first equation by 2 and the second by 3:

①×2 $6x + 10y = -8$
②×3 $-6x + 9y = 27$

Add the equations together to eliminate the x's.

$19y = 19$
$y = 1$

So y is 1. Now stick that value for y into one of the equations to find x:

$y = 1$ in ① $\Rightarrow 3x + 5 = -4$

$3x = -9$
$x = -3$

So the solution is x = –3, y = 1.

A MATCH THE COEFFICIENTS

Multiply the equations by numbers that will make either the x's or the y's match in the two equations (ignoring minus signs).

Go for the lowest common multiple (LCM). e.g. LCM of 2 and 3 is 6.

B ELIMINATE TO FIND ONE VARIABLE

If the coefficients are the _same_ sign, you'll need to _subtract_ one equation from the other.

If the coefficients are _different_ signs, you need to _add_ the equations.

C FIND THE VARIABLE YOU ELIMINATED

When you've found one variable, put its value into one of the original equations so you can find the other variable.

But you should always...

D CHECK YOUR ANSWER

...by putting these values into the other equation.

② $-2x + 3y = 9$
$x = -3$
$y = 1$

$-2 \times (-3) + 3 \times 1 = 6 + 3 = 9$

If these two numbers are the same, then the values you've got for the variables are right.

Elimination Method

1) Match the coefficients

2) Eliminate and then solve for one variable

3) Find the other variable (that you eliminated)

4) Check your answer

Eliminate your social life — do A-level maths...

This is a fairly basic method that won't be new to you, so make sure you know it. (The only possibly tricky bit is matching the coefficients — work out the lowest common multiple of the coefficients of x, say, then multiply the equations to get this number in front of each x.) I'm not kidding, you _have_ to be able to do these — they crop up in all sorts of questions.

Simultaneous Equations with Quadratics

Elimination is great for simple equations. But it won't always work. Sometimes one of the equations has not just x's and y's in it — but bits with x^2 and y^2 as well. When this happens, you can only use the substitution method.

Use Substitution if one equation is Quadratic

EXAMPLE:
$$-x + 2y = 5 \quad \text{—} \quad (L)$$
$$x^2 + y^2 = 25 \quad \text{—} \quad (Q)$$

The linear equation — with only x's and y's in.

The quadratic equation — with some x^2 and y^2 bits in.

Rearrange the linear equation so that either x or y is on its own on one side of the equals sign.

$$(L) \quad -x + 2y = 5$$
$$\Rightarrow x = 2y - 5$$

Substitute your expression from Step 1 into the quadratic equation...

Sub into (Q): $\quad x^2 + y^2 = 25$
$$\Rightarrow (2y - 5)^2 + y^2 = 25$$

...and then rearrange this into the form $ax^2 + bx + c = 0$, so you can solve it — either by factorising or using the quadratic formula.

$$\Rightarrow (4y^2 - 20y + 25) + y^2 = 25$$
$$\Rightarrow 5y^2 - 20y = 0$$
$$\Rightarrow 5y(y - 4) = 0$$
$$\Rightarrow y = 0 \text{ or } y = 4$$

One Quadratic and One Linear Eqn

1) **Isolate variable in linear equation**
   Rearrange the linear equation to get either x or y on its own.

2) **Substitute into quadratic equation**
   — to get a quadratic equation in just one variable.

3) **Solve to get values for one variable**
   — either by factorising or using the quadratic formula.

4) **Stick these values in the linear equation**
   — to find corresponding values for the other variable.

Finally put both these values back into the linear equation to find corresponding values for x:

When y = 0: $\quad -x + 2y = 5$ (L)
$$\Rightarrow x = -5$$

When y = 4: $\quad -x + 2y = 5$ (L)
$$\Rightarrow -x + 8 = 5$$
$$\Rightarrow x = 3$$

So the solutions to the simultaneous equations are: x = –5, y = 0 and x = 3, y = 4.

As usual, check your answers by putting these values back into the original equations.

CHECK YOUR ANSWERS

x=–5, y=0: $\quad -(-5) + 2 \times 0 = 5$ ✓
$$(-5)^2 + 0^2 = 25 ✓$$

x=3, y=4: $\quad -(3) + 2 \times 4 = 5$ ✓
$$3^2 + 4^2 = 25 ✓$$

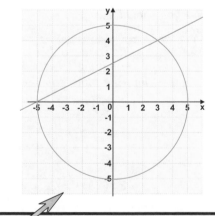

y = x² — a match-winning substitution...

The quadratic equation above is actually a circle about the origin with radius 5. (Don't worry — you don't need to know about equations of circles in Me). The linear equation is just a standard straight line. So what you're actually finding here are the two points where the line passes through the circle. And these turn out to be (–5,0) and (3,4). See the graph. (I thought you might appreciate seeing a graph that wasn't a line or a parabola for a change.)

Geometric Interpretation

When you have to interpret something <u>geometrically</u> — you have to say what you would see if you drew a picture.

Two Solutions — two points of intersection

EXAMPLE:

$$y = x^2 - 4x + 5 \quad \text{——①}$$
$$y = 2x - 3 \quad \text{——②}$$

SOLUTION: Substitute expression for y from ② into ①:

$$2x - 3 = x^2 - 4x + 5$$

Rearrange and solve:

$$x^2 - 6x + 8 = 0$$
$$(x-2)(x-4) = 0$$
$$x = 2 \text{ or } x = 4$$

Putting these in ② gives:

$$x = 2 \Rightarrow y = 2 \times 2 - 3 = 1$$
$$x = 4 \Rightarrow y = 2 \times 4 - 3 = 5$$

There's 2 pairs of solutions: $x = 2$, $y = 1$ and $x = 4$, $y = 5$

GEOMETRIC INTERPRETATION:

So from solving the simultaneous equations, you know that the graphs meet in <u>two places</u> — the points (2,1) and (4,5).

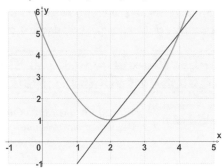

One Solution — one point of intersection

EXAMPLE:

$$y = x^2 - 4x + 5 \quad \text{——①}$$
$$y = 2x - 4 \quad \text{——②}$$

SOLUTION: Substitute ② in ①: $\quad 2x - 4 = x^2 - 4x + 5$

Rearrange and solve:

$$x^2 - 6x + 9 = 0$$
$$(x-3)^2 = 0$$
$$x = 3$$

Double root i.e. you only get 1 solution from the quadratic.

Putting this in ② gives:

$$y = 2 \times 3 - 4$$
$$y = 2$$

There's 1 solution: $x = 3$, $y = 2$

GEOMETRIC INTERPRETATION:

Since the equations have only one solution, the two graphs only meet at one point — (3,2). The straight line is a <u>tangent</u> to the curve.

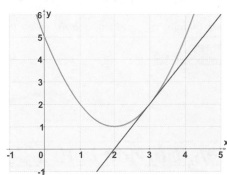

No Solutions means the graphs Never Meet

EXAMPLE:

$$y = x^2 - 4x + 5 \quad \text{——①}$$
$$y = 2x - 5 \quad \text{——②}$$

SOLUTION: Substitute ② in ①: $\quad 2x - 5 = x^2 - 4x + 5$

Rearrange and try to solve with the quadratic formula:

$$x^2 - 6x + 10 = 0$$
$$b^2 - 4ac = (-6)^2 - 4 \times 10$$
$$= 36 - 40 = -4$$

$b^2 - 4ac < 0$, so the quadratic has no roots.
So the simultaneous equations have no solutions.

GEOMETRIC INTERPRETATION:

The equations have no solutions — the graphs never meet.

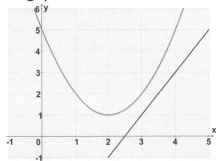

Geometric Interpretation? Frankly my dear, I don't give a damn...

What do solutions make? Intersections, that's what. If you don't find a solution, you ain't never gonna find an intersection...

Linear Inequalities

Solving _inequalities_ is very similar to solving equations. You've just got to be really careful that you keep the inequality sign pointing the _right_ way.

> Find the ranges of x that satisfy these inequalities:
> **(i)** $x - 3 < -1 + 2x$ **(ii)** $8x + 2 \geq 2x + 17$ **(iii)** $4 - 3x \leq 16$ **(iv)** $36x < 6x^2$

Sometimes the inequality sign Changes Direction

Like I said, these are pretty similar to solving equations — because whatever you do to one side, you have to do to the other. But multiplying or dividing by _negative_ numbers _changes_ the direction of the inequality sign.

Adding or Subtracting doesn't change the direction of the inequality sign

EXAMPLE: If you _add_ or _subtract_ something from both sides of an inequality, the inequality sign _doesn't_ change direction.

Adding 1 to both sides leaves the inequality sign pointing in the same direction.

Subtracting x from both sides doesn't affect the inequality.

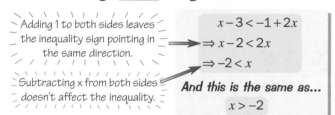

$$x - 3 < -1 + 2x$$
$$\Rightarrow x - 2 < 2x$$
$$\Rightarrow -2 < x$$

And this is the same as...

$$x > -2$$

Multiplying or Dividing by something Positive doesn't affect the inequality sign

EXAMPLE: Multiplying or dividing both sides of an inequality by a _positive_ number _doesn't_ affect the direction of the inequality sign.

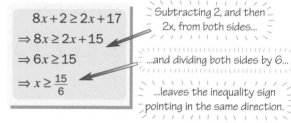

$$8x + 2 \geq 2x + 17$$
$$\Rightarrow 8x \geq 2x + 15$$
$$\Rightarrow 6x \geq 15$$
$$\Rightarrow x \geq \frac{15}{6}$$

Subtracting 2, and then 2x, from both sides...

...and dividing both sides by 6...

...leaves the inequality sign pointing in the same direction.

But Change the inequality if you Multiply or Divide by something Negative

But multiplying or dividing both sides of an inequality by a _negative_ number _changes_ the direction of the inequality.

EXAMPLE:

$$4 - 3x \leq 16$$
$$\Rightarrow -3x \leq 12$$
$$\Rightarrow x \geq -4$$

Subtract 4 from both sides.

Then divide both sides by -3 — but _change_ the direction of the inequality.

> The _reason_ for the sign changing direction is because it's just the same as swapping everything from one side to the other:
> $$-3x \leq -12 \Rightarrow 12 \leq 3x \Rightarrow x \geq 4$$

Don't divide both sides by Variables — like x and y

You've got to be really careful when you divide by things that _might_ be negative — well basically, don't do it.

EXAMPLE: $36x < 6x^2$

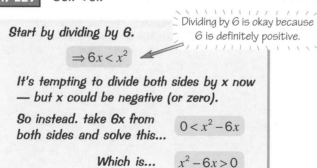

Start by dividing by 6.

$$\Rightarrow 6x < x^2$$

Dividing by 6 is okay because 6 is definitely positive.

It's tempting to divide both sides by x now — but x could be negative (or zero).

So instead. take 6x from both sides and solve this...

$$0 < x^2 - 6x$$

Which is... $x^2 - 6x > 0$

Two types of inequality sign

There are two kinds of inequality sign:

Type 1: $<$ — less than

$>$ — greater than

Type 2: $\leq$ — less than or equal to

$\geq$ — greater than or equal to

Whatever type the question uses — use the same kind all the way through your answer.

See the next page for more on solving quadratic inequalities.

So no one knows we've arrived safely — splendid...

So just remember — inequalities are just like normal equations except that you have to reverse the sign when multiplying or dividing by a negative number. And _don't_ divide both sides by variables. OK — lecture's over.

Quadratic Inequalities

With quadratic inequalities, you're best off drawing the __graph__ and taking it from there.

Draw a Graph to solve a Quadratic inequality

EXAMPLE: Find the ranges of x which satisfy these inequalities:

① $-x^2 + 2x + 4 \geq 1$

② $2x^2 - x - 3 > 0$

First rewrite the inequality with __zero__ on one side.

$$-x^2 + 2x + 3 \geq 0$$

Then __draw__ the graph of $y = -x^2 + 2x + 3$:

So find where it crosses the x-axis (i.e. where y = 0):

$$-x^2 + 2x + 3 = 0 \implies x^2 - 2x - 3 = 0$$
$$\implies (x+1)(x-3) = 0$$
$$\implies x = -1 \text{ or } x = 3$$

And the coefficient of x^2 is negative, so the graph is n-shaped. It looks like this:

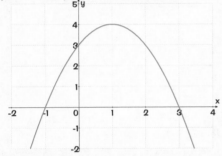

You're interested in when this is __positive or zero__, i.e. when it's above the x-axis.

From the graph, this is when x is __between –1 and 3__ (including those points). So your answer is...

$$-x^2 + 2x + 4 \geq 1 \text{ when } -1 \leq x \leq 3.$$

This one already has zero on one side, so __draw__ the graph of $y = 2x^2 - x - 3$.

Find where it crosses the x-axis:

$$2x^2 - x - 3 = 0$$
$$\implies (2x-3)(x+1)$$
$$\implies x = \tfrac{3}{2} \text{ or } x = -1$$

Factorise it to find the roots.

And the coefficient of x^2 is positive, so the graph is u-shaped, and looks like this:

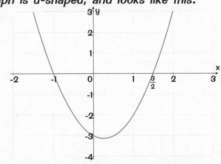

You need to say when this is __positive__. Looking at the graph, there are two parts of the x-axis where this is true — when x is __less than –1__ and when x is __greater than 3/2__. So your answer is:

$$2x^2 - x - 3 > 0 \text{ when } x < -1 \text{ or } x > \tfrac{3}{2}.$$

EXAMPLE (REVISITED): On the last page you had to solve $36x < 6x^2$.

$$36x < 6x^2$$

Equation 1 $\implies 6x < x^2$

$$\implies 0 < x^2 - 6x$$

So draw the graph of $y = x^2 - 6x = x(x-6)$

And this is __positive__ when $x < 0$ or $x > 6$.

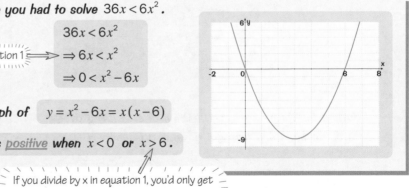

If you divide by x in equation 1, you'd only get half the solution — you'd miss the x < 0 part.

That's nonsense — I can see perfectly...

Call me sad, but I reckon these questions are pretty cool. They look a lot more difficult than they actually are and you get to draw a picture. Wow! When you do the graph, the important thing is to find where it crosses the x-axis (you don't need to know where it crosses the y-axis) and make sure you draw it the right way up. Then you just need to decide which bit of the graph you want. It'll either be the range(s) of x where the graph is below the x-axis or the range(s) where it's above. And this depends on the inequality sign.

Section Three — Simultaneous Equations, Inequalities and Geometry

Coordinate Geometry

Coordinate geometry is really just about... errm... Oh, I don't know. I was trying to think of a really easy way to explain it, so that you'd understand it straight away. But I can't. Coordinate Geometry is just more maths, of course.

Finding the equation of a line Through Two Points

If you get through your exam without having to find the equation of a line through two points, I'm a Rhinoceros.

EXAMPLE: Find the equation of the line that passes through the points (–3, 10) and (1, 4), and write it in the forms:

$$y - y_1 = m(x - x_1)$$

$$y = mx + c$$

$$ax + by + c = 0$$

— where a, b and c are _integers_.

You might be asked to write the equation of a line in _any_ of these forms — but they're all similar.
Basically, if you find an equation in one form — you can easily _convert_ it into either of the others.

The _Easiest_ to find is $y - y_1 = m(x - x_1)$...

Point 1 is (–3, 10) and Point 2 is (1, 4)

LABEL THE POINTS Label Point 1 as (x_1, y_1) and Point 2 as (x_2, y_2).

Point 1 — $(x_1, y_1) = (-3, 10)$

Point 2 — $(x_2, y_2) = (1, 4)$

> It doesn't matter which way round you label them.

FIND THE GRADIENT Find the _gradient_ of the line m — this is $m = \dfrac{y_2 - y_1}{x_2 - x_1}$.

$$m = \frac{4-10}{1-(-3)} = \frac{-6}{4} = -\frac{3}{2}$$

WRITE DOWN THE EQUATION _Write down_ the equation of the line, using the coordinates x_1 and y_1 — this is just $y - y_1 = m(x - x_1)$.

$x_1 = -3$ and $y_1 = 10$ $\implies$ $y - 10 = -\dfrac{3}{2}(x - (-3))$

$$y - 10 = -\frac{3}{2}(x + 3)$$

...and _Rearrange_ this to get the other two forms:

For the form $y = mx + c$, take everything except the y over to the right.

$$y - 10 = -\frac{3}{2}(x + 3)$$

$$\Rightarrow y = -\frac{3}{2}x - \frac{9}{2} + 10$$

$$\Rightarrow y = -\frac{3}{2}x + \frac{11}{2}$$

To find the form $ax + by + c = 0$, take everything over to one side — and then get rid of any fractions.

> Multiply the whole equation by 2 to get rid of the 2's on the bottom line.

$$y = -\frac{3}{2}x + \frac{11}{2}$$

$$\Rightarrow \frac{3}{2}x + y - \frac{11}{2} = 0$$

$$\Rightarrow 3x + 2y - 11 = 0$$

Equations of Lines

1) **LABEL** the points (x_1, y_1) and (x_2, y_2).

2) **GRADIENT** — find it and call it m.

3) **WRITE DOWN THE EQUATION** using $y - y_1 = m(x - x_1)$.

4) **CONVERT** to one of the other forms, if necessary.

> If you end up with an equation like $\frac{3}{2}x - \frac{4}{3}y + 6 = 0$, where you've got a 2 and a 3 on the bottom of the fractions — multiply everything by the _lowest common multiple_ of 2 and 3, i.e. 6.

There ain't nuffink to this geometry lark, Mister...

This is the sort of stuff that looks hard but is actually pretty easy. Finding the equation of a line in that first form really is a piece of cake — the only thing you have to be careful of is when a point has a negative coordinate (or two). In that case, you've just got to make sure you do the subtractions properly when you work out the gradient. See, this stuff ain't so bad...

Coordinate Geometry

More simple stuff for you to have a go at. It's all stuff you've done before, but this time it's used in a different way.

Find the Midpoint by Averaging each of the coordinates

Don't complain. It doesn't get any easier than this.

EXAMPLE: Find the midpoint of AB, where A and B are (–3, 10) and (1, 4) respectively.

Find the midpoint by taking the average of the x- and y-coordinates:

Label the points (x_1, y_1) and (x_2, y_2).

Average x-coordinate = $\dfrac{x_1 + x_2}{2} = \dfrac{-3+1}{2} = -1$

These are the midpoint coordinates.

Average y-coordinate = $\dfrac{y_1 + y_2}{2} = \dfrac{10+4}{2} = 7$

So the midpoint has coordinates $(-1, 7)$.

Finding where lines meet means solving Simultaneous Equations

Okay, you can complain now. This is no fun at all.

Two lines...

Line l_1	Line l_2
$5x + 2y - 9 = 0$	$3x + 4y - 4 = 0$
$y = -\dfrac{5}{2}x + \dfrac{9}{2}$	$y = -\dfrac{3}{4}x + 1$

EXAMPLE: Find where the line l_1 meets the line l_2.

$5x + 2y - 9 = 0$ ——①
$3x + 4y - 4 = 0$ ——②

Finding where the lines meet means solving these simultaneous equations.

$10x + 4y - 18 = 0$ ——③ $= 2 \times$①

$7x - 14 = 0$ ——③ – ②

$\Rightarrow x = 2$

Putting this back into equation ② then gives...

$(3 \times 2) + 4y - 4 = 0$

$\Rightarrow 6 + 4y - 4 = 0$

$\Rightarrow 4y = -2$

$\Rightarrow y = -\dfrac{1}{2}$

So the lines meet at the point $\left(2, -\dfrac{1}{2}\right)$.

If you've got the equations in the form $y = mx + c$ — make the right-hand sides of both equations equal.

Line l_1: $y = -\dfrac{5}{2}x + \dfrac{9}{2}$ Line l_2: $y = -\dfrac{3}{4}x + 1$

$-\dfrac{5}{2}x + \dfrac{9}{2} = -\dfrac{3}{4}x + 1$

Solve this equation to find a value for x.

$\Rightarrow -\dfrac{7}{4}x = -\dfrac{7}{2}$

$\Rightarrow x = 2$

Then put this value of x into one of the equations to find the y-coordinate...

$y = -\dfrac{5}{2} \times 2 + \dfrac{9}{2}$

It doesn't matter which of the equations you use.

$y = -\dfrac{1}{2}$

So the lines meet at the point $\left(2, -\dfrac{1}{2}\right)$.

And I think to myself — what a wonderful page...

What an absolutely superb page. There it is, above all these words that you never read. It's fuller than a student at an all-you-can-eat curry house — absolutely jam- (or madras-) packed with useful things about simultaneous equations and midpoints. Learn this lot, get a few more marks, get the grades you need, and get yourself into some more all-you-can-eat curry houses.

Section Three — Simultaneous Equations, Inequalities and Geometry

Coordinate Geometry

This page is based around two really important facts that you've got to know — one about parallel lines, one about perpendicular lines. It's really a page of unparalleled excitement...

Two more lines...

Line l_1
$3x - 4y - 7 = 0$
$y = \frac{3}{4}x - \frac{7}{4}$

Line l_2
$x - 3y - 3 = 0$
$y = \frac{1}{3}x - 1$

...and two points...

Point A $(3, -1)$
Point B $(-2, 4)$

Parallel lines have equal Gradient

> **EXAMPLE:** Find the line parallel to l_1 that passes through the point A (3, –1).

Parallel lines have the <u>same gradient</u>.

The original equation is this: $y = \frac{3}{4}x - \frac{7}{4}$

So the new equation will be this: $y = \frac{3}{4}x + c$

We just need to find c.

We know that the line passes through A, so at this point x will be 3, and y will be –1.

Stick these values into the equation to find c.

$$-1 = \frac{3}{4} \times 3 + c$$

$$\Rightarrow c = -1 - \frac{9}{4} = -\frac{13}{4}$$

So the equation of the line is... $y = \frac{3}{4}x - \frac{13}{4}$

And if you're only given the ax + by + c = 0 form it's even easier:

The <u>original</u> line is: $3x - 4y - 7 = 0$

So the <u>new</u> line is: $3x - 4y + k = 0$

Then just use the values of x and y at the point A to find k...

$$3 \times 3 - 4 \times (-1) - k = 0$$

$$\Rightarrow 13 - k = 0$$

$$\Rightarrow k = 13$$

So the equation is: $3x - 4y - 13 = 0$

The gradient of a Perpendicular line is: –1 ÷ the Other Gradient

Finding <u>perpendicular</u> lines (or '<u>normals</u>') is just as easy as finding parallel lines — as long as you remember the gradient of the perpendicular line is <u>–1 ÷ the gradient of the other one</u>.

> **EXAMPLE:** Find the line perpendicular to l_2 that passes through the point B (–2, 4).

l_2 has equation: $y = \frac{1}{3}x - 1$

So if the equation of the new line is $y = mx + c$, then

$$m = -1 \div \frac{1}{3}$$

$$\Rightarrow m = -3$$

Since the gradient of a perpendicular line is: –1 ÷ the other one.

Also...
$$4 = (-3) \times (-2) + c$$
$$\Rightarrow c = 4 - 6 = -2$$

Putting the coordinates of B(–2, 4) into y = –3x + c.

So the equation of the line is...

$$y = -3x - 2$$

Or if you start with: l_2 $x - 3y - 3 = 0$

To find a perpendicular line, swap these two numbers around, and change the sign of <u>one of them</u>. (So here, 1 and –3 become 3 and 1.)

So the new line has equation...
$$3x + y + d = 0$$
Or you could have used –3x – y + d = 0.

But...
$$3 \times (-2) + 4 + d = 0$$
$$\Rightarrow d = 2$$

Using the coordinates of point B.

And so the equation of the <u>perpendicular</u> line is...

$$3x + y + 2 = 0$$

Wowzers — parallel lines on the same graph dimension...

This looks more complicated than it actually is, all this tangent and normal business. All you're doing is finding the equation of a straight line through a certain point — the only added complication is that you have to find the gradient first. And there's another way to remember how to find the gradient of a normal — just remember that the gradients of perpendicular lines multiply together to make –1.

__Section Three Revision Questions__

What's that I hear you cry? You want revision questions — and lots of them. Well, it just so happens I've got a few here. Loads of questions on simultaneous equations, inequalities and coordinate geometry. With simultaneous equations — well, just don't rush them — or you'll spend twice as long looking for ~~milkshakes~~ mistakes as it took you to do the question in the first place. With inequalities, just remember to be careful when you're multiplying or dividing. But, as far as the old favourite geometry goes, my advice is — 'if you're not sure, draw a picture — even if it's not accurate'.

1) A jolly start — not. Solve these sets of simultaneous equations.

   a) $3x - 4y = 7$ and $-2x + 7y = -22$ b) $2x - 3y = \frac{11}{12}$ and $x + y = -\frac{7}{12}$

2) Find where possible (and that's a bit of a clue) the solutions to these sets of simultaneous equations. Interpret your answers geometrically.

     a) $y = x^2 - 7x + 4$ b) $y = 30 - 6x + 2x^2$ c) $x^2 + 2y^2 - 3 = 0$

         $2x - y - 10 = 0$ $y = 2(x + 11)$ $y = 2x + 4$

3) Find the ranges of x that satisfy these inequalities: i) $x + 6 < 5x - 4$ ii) $4x - 2 > x - 14$ iii) $7 - x \le 4 - 2x$

4) Find the ranges of x that satisfy these jokers: i) $x^2 + 3x - 1 \ge x + 2$ ii) $2x^2 > x + 1$ iii) $3x^2 - 12 < x^2 - 2x$

5) Find the equations of the straight lines that go through the points   a) $(2, -1)$ and $(-4, -19)$,   b) $(0, -\frac{1}{3})$ and $(5, \frac{2}{3})$.

   Write each of them in the forms
   i) $y - y_1 = m(x - x_1)$ ii) $y = mx + c$ iii) $ax + by + c = 0$, where a, b and c are integers.

6) Find the point that lies midway between:
   a) $(3, -1)$ and $(-4, 3)$ b) $(10, 4)$ and $(2, 11)$ c) $(96, 9)$ and $(103, 8)$

7) A bit trickier: find where the following lines meet: a) $y = 3x - 4$ and $y = 7x - 5$,
   b) $y = 13 - 2x$ and $7x - y - 23 = 0$,   c) $2x - 3y + 4 = 0$ and $x - 2y + 1 = 0$.

8) a) The line l has equation $y = \frac{3}{2}x - \frac{2}{3}$. Find the equation of the lovely, cuddly line parallel to l, passing through the point with coordinates $(4, 2)$. Name this line Lily.

   b) The line m (whose name is actually Mike) passes through the point $(6, 1)$ and is perpendicular to $2x - y - 7 = 0$. What is the equation of m?

9) The points A, B and C have coordinates $(1, 4)$, $(4, 5)$ and $(3, 9)$ respectively, and D is the midpoint of BC. Find the equation of the line passing through points A and D.

10) The coordinates of points R and S are $(1, 10)$ and $(9, 3)$ respectively. Find the equation of the line perpendicular to RS, passing through the point midway between them.

11) Find the equation of your washing line, given that it passes through the origin.

Differentiation

Brrrrr... differentiation is a bad one — it really is. Not because it's that hard, but because in the exams it comes up all over the place, every time. So if you don't know it perfectly, you're asking for trouble.

Derivative just means 'the thing you get when you differentiate something'.

$$\frac{d}{dx}\left(x^n\right) = nx^{n-1}$$

$\frac{d}{dx}$ just means 'the derivative of the thing in the brackets'.

Use this formula to differentiate *Powers of x*

EXAMPLE: Differentiate y when:

    i) $y = x^5$ ii) $y = 6x^3$ iii) $y = 24x$ iv) $y = 5$

i) $y = x^5$

n is just the power of x.

Here, $n = 5$

So $\dfrac{dy}{dx} = nx^{n-1} = 5x^4$

ii) $y = 6x^3$

$$\frac{dy}{dx} = 6\left(3x^2\right)$$

i.e. $\dfrac{dy}{dx} = 18x^2$

$$\frac{d(af(x))}{dx} = a\frac{d(f(x))}{dx}$$

— i.e. you ignore the number and only worry about the x bit.

iii) $y = 24x$

When you've only got x (which is x^1)...

$$\frac{dy}{dx} = 24\left(1.x^0\right)$$

i.e. $\dfrac{dy}{dx} = 24$

...you just end up with the coefficient of x.

iv) $y = 5$

You need every term to be a power of x to differentiate.

$$\Rightarrow y = 5x^0$$

$$\Rightarrow \frac{dy}{dx} = 5(0x^{-1}) = 0$$

Isolated numbers and constants just disappear when you differentiate.

Differentiate each term in an equation *Separately*

This formula is better than cake — even better than that really nice sticky black chocolate one from that place in town. Even if there are loads of terms in the equation, it doesn't matter. Differentiate each bit separately and you'll be fine.

You can do this because:

$$\frac{d(f(x)+g(x))}{dx} = \frac{d(f(x))}{dx} + \frac{d(g(x))}{dx}$$

EXAMPLE:

Differentiate y when: i) $y = 6x^4 + 4x^3 - 2x + 1$ ii) $y = (x+2)(x+3)$

i) For equations like this...

$$y = 6x^4 + 4x^3 - 2x + 1$$

...just differentiate each term separately.

$$\frac{dy}{dx} = 6\left(4x^3\right) + 4\left(3x^2\right) - 2 + 0$$

$$\frac{dy}{dx} = 24x^3 + 12x^2 - 2$$

ii) You can't differentiate it until it's written as separate terms which are all powers of x.

$$y = (x+2)(x+3)$$

So multiply out the brackets...

$$y = x^2 + 5x + 6$$

Then it's easy: $\dfrac{dy}{dx} = 2x + 5$

Dario Gradient — differentiating Crewe from the rest...

If you're going to do maths, you've got to be able to differentiate things. Simple as that. But luckily, once you can do the simple stuff, you should be all right. Big long equations are just made up of loads of simple little terms, so they're no really that much harder. Learn the formula, and make sure you can use it by practising all day and all night forever.

Differentiation

But what's the point of differentiation? I dunno. Search me...

Differentiating a function gives you its Gradient

Differentiating a function (a curve, say) gives you an __expression__ for the gradient of the curve.
Then you can find the gradient of the curve at any point by substituting for x.

EXAMPLE: Find the gradient of the graph $y = x^2$ at $x = 1$ and $x = -2$...

Differentiate to get the gradient:

$$\frac{dy}{dx} = 2x$$

Now when $x = 1$, $\frac{dy}{dx} = 2$

And so the gradient of the graph at x = 1 is 2.

And when $x = -2$, $\frac{dy}{dx} = -4$

So the gradient of the graph at x = -2 is -4.

The gradient of a __curve__ is the same as the gradient of the __tangent__ at that point.

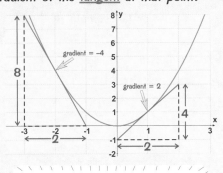

gradient = -4

gradient = 2

A __tangent__ is a line that just touches a curve without actually going through it.

Find out if a function is Increasing or Decreasing

You can also use differentiation to work out exactly where a function is _increasing_ or _decreasing_.
And you can use it to find out its _rate of change_ — that's how fast it's decreasing or increasing.

A function is _increasing_ when...
...the gradient is _positive_.

y gets bigger...

...as x gets bigger.

A function is _decreasing_ when...
...the gradient is _negative_.

y gets smaller...

...as x gets bigger.

The _bigger_ the gradient...
...the _faster_ y changes with x.

A small change in x means a big change in y.

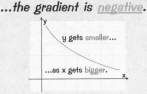

A big change in x means a small change in y.

EXAMPLE: Find where the following function is _increasing_ and _decreasing_: $f(x) = 3x^2 - 6x$.

This is a question about _gradients_ — so _differentiate_.

$$f(x) = 3x^2 - 6x$$
$$\Rightarrow f'(x) = 6x - 6$$

f'(x) (pronounced, 'f-dash of x' or 'f-prime of x') is another way to write the derivative.

This is an _increasing_ function when

$$6x - 6 > 0$$
$$\Rightarrow x > 1$$

This is a _decreasing_ function when

$$6x - 6 < 0$$
$$\Rightarrow x < 1$$

Differentiation and Gradients

To find the gradient of a curve at a certain point:
1) Differentiate the equation of the curve.
2) Work out the derivative at the point.

An increasing function has a _positive_ gradient.

A decreasing function has a _negative_ gradient.

Help me Differentiation — You're my only hope...

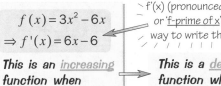

I'm gonna get a bit heavy here, but understanding the idea of using differentiation to find the gradient of a graph is more important than washing regularly — AND THAT'S IMPORTANT. The __gradient__ thing should set bells ringing — if the gradient of a graph tells you the rate of change of one thing with respect to another, that means __dy/dx is the rate of change of y with respect to x__. That's the longhand way of saying it, but if you think of it like that, it's tonnes easier to remember the relationship between __positive__ derivatives and __increasing__ functions (and vice versa).

Differentiation

To find a _stationary point_, you need to find where the graph 'levels off' — that means where the _gradient_ becomes _zero_.

Stationary Points are when the gradient is Zero

EXAMPLE: Find the stationary points on the curve $y = 2x^3 - 3x^2 - 12x + 5$, and work out the nature of each one.

A _stationary point_ can be...

(i) a _maximum_,

or (iii) something like _this_.

(ii) a _minimum_,

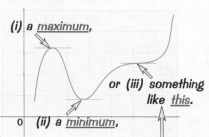

At stationary points, the gradient = 0, which means $\frac{dy}{dx} = 0$.

This kind of stationary point is called a 'point of inflection'.

A 'turning point' is a another name for a maximum or a minimum.

You need to find where $\frac{dy}{dx} = 0$. So first, _differentiate_ the function.

$$y = 2x^3 - 3x^2 - 12x + 5$$
$$\Rightarrow \frac{dy}{dx} = 6x^2 - 6x - 12$$

This is the expression for the gradient.

And then set this derivative equal to _zero_.

$$6x^2 - 6x - 12 = 0$$
$$\Rightarrow x^2 - x - 2 = 0$$
$$\Rightarrow (x - 2)(x + 1) = 0$$
$$\Rightarrow x = 2 \text{ or } x = -1$$

See pages 5 to 9 for more about solving quadratics.

So the graph has _two_ stationary points, at $x = 2$ and $x = -1$.

Looking at the Gradient will tell you if it's a Maximum or a Minimum

Once you've found where the stationary points are, you have to decide whether each of them is a _maximum_ or _minimum_ — that's all a question means when it says, '...determine the _nature_ of the turning points'.

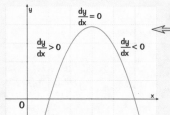

$\frac{dy}{dx} = 0$

$\frac{dy}{dx} > 0$ $\frac{dy}{dx} < 0$

If it's a **MAXIMUM**, the gradient goes from positive to zero to negative.

If it's a **MINIMUM**, the gradient goes from negative to zero to positive. ⟹

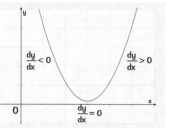

$\frac{dy}{dx} < 0$ $\frac{dy}{dx} > 0$

$\frac{dy}{dx} = 0$

So going back to the example:

x = −1 — MAX OR MIN?

Stick in numbers just left and just right and see how the sign of the gradient changes.

$$x = -1.2 \Rightarrow \frac{dy}{dx} = 6(-1.2)^2 - 6(-1.2) - 12$$
$$= 3.84 \ (+ve)$$

$$x = -0.8 \Rightarrow \frac{dy}{dx} = 6(-0.8)^2 - 6(-0.8) - 12$$
$$= -3.36 \ (-ve)$$

So the gradient goes from positive to negative, which means $x = -1$ is a _maximum_.

x = 2 — MAX OR MIN?

Same thing again:

$$x = 1.9 \Rightarrow \frac{dy}{dx} = 6(1.9)^2 - 6(1.9) - 12$$
$$= -1.74 \ (-ve)$$

$$x = 2.1 \Rightarrow \frac{dy}{dx} = 6(2.1)^2 - 6(2.1) - 12$$
$$= 1.86 \ (+ve)$$

So the gradient goes from negative to positive, which means $x = 2$ is a _minimum_.

This page could be a real turning point in your life...

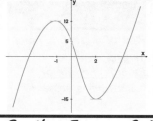

⟸ So this is what the curve $y = 2x^3 - 3x^2 - 12x + 5$ looks like (_cubics_ often have 2 turning points, quadratics only have one).

The example on this page is a pretty standard question (or part of question), so make sure you learn the method. The last bit is a bit weird — you have to choose numbers _close_ to the turning points. If they're not close enough, you could get weird results. (If you picked −3 and 3 in this example for the −1 turning point, you'd get positive gradients either side. So be careful, ay.)

Integration

Integration is the 'opposite' of differentiation — and so if you can differentiate, you can be pretty confident you'll be able to integrate too. There's just one extra thing you have to remember — the constant of integration...

You need the constant because there's More Than One right answer

When you integrate something, you're trying to find a function that returns to what you started with when you differentiate it. And when you add the constant of integration, you're just allowing for the fact that there's _more_ than one possible function that does this...

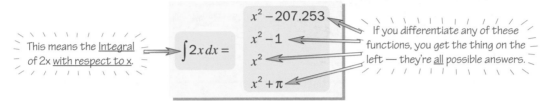

This means the Integral of 2x with respect to x.

$$\int 2x\,dx =$$

$$x^2 - 207.253$$
$$x^2 - 1$$
$$x^2$$
$$x^2 + \pi$$

If you differentiate any of these functions, you get the thing on the left — they're _all_ possible answers.

So the answer to this integral is actually...

$$\int 2x\,dx = x^2 + C$$

The '_C_' just means '_any number_'. This is the _constant of integration_.

You only need to add a constant of integration to _indefinite integrals_ — these are just integrals without _limits_ (or little numbers) next to the integral sign. (If that doesn't make sense, you'll see what I mean later on.)

Up the power by One — then Divide by it

This is an indefinite integral — it doesn't have any limits (numbers) next to the integral sign.

$$\int x^n dx = \frac{x^{n+1}}{n+1} + C$$

In a nutshell, this says:

> To integrate a power of x: (i) Increase the power by one
> — then divide by it.
> and (ii) Stick a constant on the end.

EXAMPLES: Integrate the following with respect to x:
i) x^3 ii) $3x^2 - 2x + 7$ iii) $x^2(x-4)$

$$\int 24x^4 dx = 24\int x^4 dx$$

— i.e. you ignore the number bit in each term and only worry about the x bit.
(Just like differentiation.)

i)
$$\int x^3 dx = \frac{x^4}{4} + C$$

Increase the power to 4... ...and then divide by 4.

ii) Do each term separately (like with differentiation).

$$\int(3x^2 - 2x + 7)dx$$
$$= \frac{3x^3}{3} - \frac{2x^2}{2} + \frac{7x}{1} + C$$
$$= x^3 - x^2 + 7x + C$$

$$\int(f(x)+g(x))dx = \int f(x)dx + \int g(x)dx$$

— i.e. you can integrate a long expression term by term.
(Just like differentiation.)

iii) Multiply it out first to get separate powers of x terms.

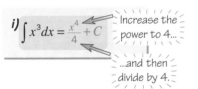

$$\int(x^2(x-4))dx$$
$$= \int(x^3 - 4x^2)dx$$
$$= \frac{x^4}{4} - \frac{4x^3}{3} + C$$

Indefinite integrals — joy without limits...

This integration lark isn't so bad then — there's only a couple of things to remember and then you can do it no problem. But that constant of integration catches loads of people out — it's so easy to forget — and you'll definitely lose marks if you do forget it. You have been warned. Other than that, there's not much to it. Hurray.

Integration

By now, you're probably aware that maths isn't something you do unless you're a bit of a _thrill-seeker_.
Sometimes they even ask you to find a curve with a certain derivative that goes through a certain point.

You sometimes need to find the _Value_ of the _Constant of Integration_

When they tell you something else about a curve in addition to its derivative, you can work out the value of the _constant of integration_. Usually the something is the _coordinates_ of one of the points the curve goes through.

REALLY IMPORTANT BIT...

When you differentiate y, you get $\frac{dy}{dx}$.
And when you integrate $\frac{dy}{dx}$, you get y*.

*If you ignore the constant of integration.

EXAMPLE: Find the equation of the curve through the point (2, 8) with $\frac{dy}{dx} = 6x(x-1)$.

You know the derivative and need to find the function — so _integrate_.

> **REMEMBER:**
> Even if you _don't_ have any extra information about the curve — you still have to add a _constant_ when you work out an integral _without limits_.

$$\frac{dy}{dx} = 6x(x-1) = 6x^2 - 6x$$

So integrating both sides gives...

$$y = \int (6x^2 - 6x)\,dx$$
$$\Rightarrow y = \frac{6x^3}{3} - \frac{6x^2}{2} + C$$
$$\Rightarrow y = 2x^3 - 3x^2 + C$$

~ Don't forget the constant of integration.

Check this is right by differentiating it and making sure you get what you started with.

$$y = 2x^3 - 3x^2 + C$$
$$\Rightarrow \frac{dy}{dx} = 2(3x^2) - 3(2x^1)$$
$$\Rightarrow \frac{dy}{dx} = 6x^2 - 6x$$

So this function's got the right derivative — but you haven't finished yet.

You now need to _find C_ — and you do this by using the fact that it goes through the point (2, 8).

$$y = 2x^3 - 3x^2 + C$$

Putting x = 2 and y = 8 in the above equation gives...

$$8 = (2 \times 2^3) - (3 \times 2^2) + C$$
$$\Rightarrow 8 = 16 - 12 + C$$
$$\Rightarrow C = 4$$

So the answer you need is this one:

$$y = 2x^3 - 3x^2 + 4$$

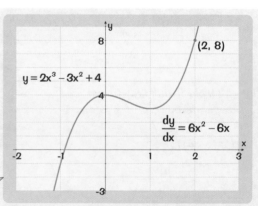

~ It's a cubic equation — and the graph looks like this...

Constant integration — my idea of heaven...

That's another page under your belt and — go on, admit it — there was nothing too horrendous on it. If you can do the stuff from the previous page and then substitute some numbers into an equation, you can do everything from this page too. So if you think this is much harder than the stuff before, you'd be wrong. Mighty wrong, in fact.

Integration

Some integrals have <u>limits</u> (i.e. little numbers) next to the integral sign. You integrate them in exactly the same way — but you <u>don't</u> need a constant of integration. Much easier. And scrummier and yummier too.

A <u>Definite Integral</u> <u>finds the</u> <u>Area Under a Curve</u>

This definite integral tells you the <u>area</u> between the graph of $y = x^3$ and the x-axis between $x = -2$ and $x = 2$:

This marks the right-hand side of the area you're finding.

Definite integrals find the area between the curve and the x-axis.

$$\int_{-2}^{2} x^3 \, dx =$$

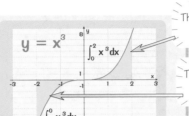

This marks the left-hand side of the area you're finding.

This area is $\int_0^2 x^3 dx = 4$. Because it's <u>positive</u>, it means the area is <u>above</u> the x-axis.

This area is $\int_{-2}^0 x^3 dx = -4$. Because it's <u>negative</u>, it means the area is <u>below</u> the x-axis.

If you work out $\int_{-2}^2 x^3 dx$, the answer will be zero, since the area below the x-axis 'cancels out' the area above.

<u>Do the integration in the same way</u> — <u>then use the</u> <u>Limits</u>

Finding a definite integral isn't really any harder than an indefinite one — there's just an <u>extra</u> stage you have to do. After you've integrated the function you have to work out the value of this new function by sticking in the <u>limits</u>.

EXAMPLE:

Evaluate $\int_1^3 (x^2 + 2) \, dx$.

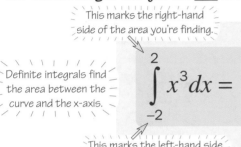

Find the integral in the normal way — then use the limits.

$$\int_1^3 (x^2 + 2) \, dx = \left[\frac{x^3}{3} + 2x \right]_1^3$$

$$= \left(\frac{3^3}{3} + 6 \right) - \left(\frac{1^3}{3} + 2 \right)$$

$$= 15 - \frac{7}{3} = \frac{38}{3}$$

Put the integrated function in <u>square brackets</u> and rewrite the limits on the right-hand side.

You <u>don't</u> need a constant of integration with a <u>definite</u> integral.

$2 = 2x^0$ — so increase the power (to 1) and divide by 1 to get 2x.

> **DEFINITE INTEGRALS**
> After you've integrated the function, put both the limits in and find the values. Then subtract what the bottom limit gave you from what the top limit gave you.

If you have to find the area under a curve between 2 vertical lines, you just take these as the limits for your integral.

EXAMPLE: Find the area between the curve $y = -3x^2 - 9$, the x-axis, the y-axis and the line $x = 2$.

Draw a quick sketch to see what you're doing:

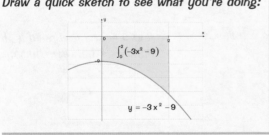

$$A = \int_0^2 (-3x^2 - 9)$$

$$= -3 \int_0^2 (x^2 + 3)$$

$$= -3 \left[\frac{x^3}{3} + 3x \right]_0^2$$

$$= -3 \left(\frac{8}{3} + 6 \right) - (0 + 0)$$

$$= -26$$

You want the area between the lines $x = 0$ and $x = 2$, so these are your limits.

Take the factor -3 outside the integral sign to make it a bit simpler.

You get a negative answer — that's just because the area is below the x-axis. So the answer is 26.

<u>More Integration... what can you say, hmmm yeah, integration...</u>

It's still integration — but this time you're putting two numbers into an equation afterwards. So although this may not be the wild and crazy fun-packed time your teachers promised you when they were trying to persuade you to take A-level maths, you've got to admit that a lot of this stuff is pretty similar — and if you can do one bit, you can use that to do quite a few other bits too. Maths is like that. But I admit it's probably not as much fun as a big banana-and-toffee cake.

Areas Between Curves

With a bit of thought, you can use integration to find all kinds of areas — even ones that look quite tricky at first. The best way to work out what to do is draw a picture. Then it'll seem easier. I promise you it will.

Sometimes you have to Add integrals...

This looks pretty hard — until you draw a picture and see what it's all about.

EXAMPLE: Find the area enclosed by the curves $y = x^2$, $y = (2-x)^2$ and the x-axis.

Find out where the curves meet by <u>solving</u> $x^2 = (2-x)^2$. — they meet at $x = 1$.

You have to find area A — but you'll need to <u>split</u> it into two smaller pieces.

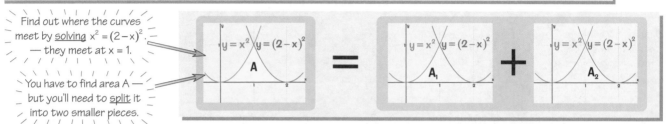

And it's pretty clear from the picture that you'll have to find the area in two lumps, A_1 and A_2.

The first area you need to find is A_1:

$$A_1 = \int_0^1 x^2 \, dx$$
$$= \left[\frac{x^3}{3}\right]_0^1$$
$$= \left(\frac{1}{3} - 0\right) = \frac{1}{3}$$

The other area you need is A_2:

$$A_2 = \int_1^2 (2-x)^2 \, dx = \int_1^2 \left(4 - 4x + x^2\right) dx$$
$$= \left[4x - 2x^2 + \frac{x^3}{3}\right]_1^2$$
$$= \left(8 - 8 + \frac{8}{3}\right) - \left(4 - 2 + \frac{1}{3}\right)$$
$$= \frac{8}{3} - \frac{7}{3} = \frac{1}{3}$$

And the area the question actually asks for is $A_1 + A_2$. This is

$$A = A_1 + A_2$$
$$= \frac{1}{3} + \frac{1}{3} = \frac{2}{3}$$

If you spot that the area A is <u>symmetrical</u> about $x = 1$, you can save yourself some work by calculating half the area and then doubling it: $A = 2\int_0^1 x^2 dx$

...sometimes you have to Subtract them

Again, it's best to look at the <u>pictures</u> to work out exactly what you need to do.

EXAMPLE: Find the area enclosed by the curve $y = 9 - x^2$ and the line $y = 5$.

Solve $9 - x^2 = 5$ to find where the graphs meet.
$9 - x^2 = 5 \Rightarrow x^2 = 4$
$\Rightarrow x = \pm\sqrt{4}$
$\Rightarrow x = \pm 2$

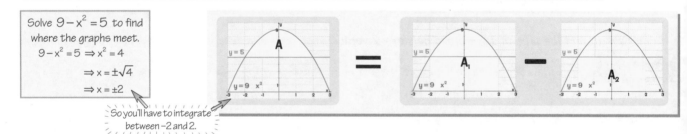

So you'll have to integrate between −2 and 2.

The area under the green curve A_1 is:

$$A_1 = \int_{-2}^{2} \left(9 - x^2\right) dx$$
$$= \left[9x - \frac{x^3}{3}\right]_{-2}^{2}$$
$$= \left(18 - \frac{2^3}{3}\right) - \left(-18 - \frac{(-2)^3}{3}\right)$$
$$= \left(18 - \frac{8}{3}\right) - \left(-18 - \left(-\frac{8}{3}\right)\right) = \frac{46}{3} - \left(-\frac{46}{3}\right) = \frac{92}{3}$$

The area under the red line is:

$$A_2 = 4 \times 5$$
$$= 20$$

And the area you need is the difference between these:

$$A = A_1 - A_2$$
$$= \frac{92}{3} - 20 = \frac{32}{3}$$

Instead of integrating before subtracting — you could try 'subtracting the lines', and then integrating. This last area A is also:
$$A = \int_{-2}^{2} \left\{\left(9 - x^2\right) - 5\right\} dx$$

And so, our hero integrates the area between two curves, and saves the day...

That's the basic idea of finding the area enclosed by two curves or lines — draw a picture and then break the area down into smaller, easier chunks. And it's always a good idea to keep an eye out for anything symmetrical that could save you a bit of work — like in the first example. Questions like this aren't hard — but they can sometimes take a long time.

Section Four Revision Questions

That's what differentiation and integration are all about. And really, if you can do one, you can also do the other. Yes, there are fiddly things to remember — like that constant of integration, for one — but overall, there are worse things you'll have to do. And just think of all the lovely marks you'll get if you can answer questions like these in the exam...

1) An easy one to start with. Write down the formula for differentiating any power of x.

2) Differentiate these functions with respect to x, and then find the gradients of the graphs at x = 1:
   a) $y = x^2 + 2$, b) $y = x^4 + 5x$, c) $y = 5x(x^2 + 3)$

3) What's the connection between the gradient of a curve y = f(x) at a point, the gradient of the tangent to the curve at the same point, and the rate of change of y with respect to x there? (That sounds like a joke in need of a punchline — but sadly, this is no joke.)

4) Not so easy — it involves inequalities: find when these two functions are increasing and decreasing:
   a) $y = 6(x + 2)(x - 3)$, b) $y = -x^2 + 3x$

5) Write down what a stationary point is. Find the stationary points of the graph $y = x(x - 8)(x - 1)$ (to 3 s.f.).

6) How can you decide whether a stationary point is a maximum or a minimum?

7) Find the stationary points of the function $y = x^3 - 3x$. Decide whether each stationary point is a minimum or a maximum.

8) Show that the lines $y = \frac{x^3}{3} - 2x^2 - 4x + \frac{86}{3}$ and $y = \frac{x^2}{32} - \frac{3}{2}$ both go through the point (4,2), and are perpendicular at that point. Good question, that — nice and exciting, just the way you like 'em.

9) Write down the steps involved in integrating a power of x.

10) What's an indefinite integral? Why do you have to add a constant of integration when you find an indefinite integral?

11) How can you check whether you've integrated something properly? (Without asking someone else.)

12) Integrate these: a) $\int 10x^4 dx$, b) $\int (3x + 5x^2) dx$, c) $\int (x^2(3x + 2)) dx$

13) Work out the equation of the curve that goes through the point (1, 0) and has derivative $\frac{dy}{dx} = 6x - 7$.

14) Find the equation of the curve that has derivative $\frac{dy}{dx} = 3x^3 + 2$ and goes through the point (1, 0). How would you change the equation if the curve had to go through the point (1, 2) instead? (Don't start the whole question again.)

15) How can you tell whether an integral is definite or indefinite? (It's easy really — it just sounds hard.)

16) What does the definite integral $\int_a^b f(x) dx$ represent on a graph?

17) Evaluate: a) $\int_{-3}^3 (9 - x^2) dx$, b) $\int_1^9 \frac{3+x}{4} dx$. Sketch the areas represented by these integrals.

18) Evaluate these definite integrals: a) $\int_0^1 (4x^3 + 3x^2 + 2x + 1) dx$, b) $\int_1^2 (10x^5 + 8x^2) dx$

19) Find the yellow area in each of these graphs:

a)
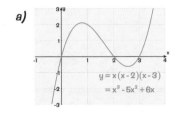
$y = x(x-2)(x-3)$
$= x^3 - 5x^2 + 6x$

b)
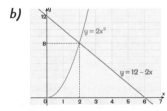
$y = 2x^2$
$y = 12 - 2x$

c)
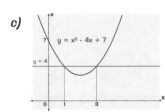
$y = x^2 - 4x + 7$
$y = 4$

Random Events and Probability

Aaahhh... a good bit of randomness comes as welcome relief in this harsh world of logic, proof and reason.
Well, it usually does. Until they make you use logic and reason to prove theories about random events. (sigh...)

A Random Event is where all Outcomes are Equally Likely

OK, start with a dice. There's always a dice in probability, like it or not. It's a simple fact of life.

When you roll a normal 6-sided dice, there are 6 possible outcomes — you could roll 1, 2, 3, 4, 5 or 6.
It's completely random what number you'll roll — each number is equally likely to come up.

EXAMPLE:

I roll two fair dice. What is the probability of
me rolling two sixes and getting past Mayfair?

There are 6 possible outcomes for each dice, so there are 6 × 6 = 36 different combinations.

There is only one favourable outcome: [6, 6]

There are 36 possible outcomes, so the
probability of getting a favourable outcome is: $P(\text{two sixes}) = \dfrac{1}{36}$

*When you roll two dice,
there are 36 possible outcomes:*
[1, 1] [1, 2] [1, 3] [1, 4] [1, 5] [1, 6]
[2, 1] [2, 2] [2, 3] [2, 4] [2, 5] [2, 6]
[3, 1] [3, 2] [3, 3] [3, 4] [3, 5] [3, 6]
[4, 1] [4, 2] [4, 3] [4, 4] [4, 5] [4, 6]
[5, 1] [5, 2] [5, 3] [5, 4] [5, 5] [5, 6]
[6, 1] [6, 2] [6, 3] [6, 4] [6, 5] [6, 6]

EXAMPLE:

What's the probability of
me getting a score of 9
and landing on Park Lane?

There are four favourable outcomes:
[3, 6], [4, 5], [5, 4], [6, 3]

There are still 36 possible outcomes, so the
probability of getting a favourable outcome is: $P(\text{score} = 9) = \dfrac{4}{36} = \dfrac{1}{9}$

Venn Diagrams help you see the Big Picture

Venn diagrams. Remember them? No? Sets? Yeaahh... course you do. *(If you don't, here's a quick reminder.)*

EXAMPLE:

I roll two fair dice. What's the probability I'll
either roll a double or roll two odd numbers?

Make S the set of all 36 possible outcomes.

Call subset A the set of outcomes where it's a double,
and B the set of outcomes where both numbers are odd.

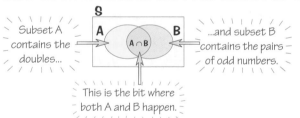

Subset A contains the doubles...

...and subset B contains the pairs of odd numbers.

This is the bit where both A and B happen.

In a set S, with subsets A and B,

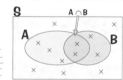

The orange bit's the intersection.

The **intersection** of A and B is everything
in both A and B, and is written $A \cap B$.

The yellow, orange and pink bits make up the union.

The **union** of A and B is everything in
either A or B, and is written $A \cup B$.

You have to take off the orange bit, or you'd be including it twice.

The union can be found using:
$A \cup B = A + B - A \cap B$

Some Basic Set Notation:

n(S) = no. of elements in S
n(A) = no. of elements in A
n(B) = no. of elements in B
n($A \cap B$) = no. of elements in both A and B
n($A \cup B$) = no. of elements in either A or B

Using the picture, you can see that the intersection, $A \cap B$,
contains the outcomes where <u>both A and B</u> occur, and the
union, $A \cup B$, contains those where <u>either A or B</u> occur.

So it's the union that you want:

$A = \{[1,1], [2,2], [3,3], [4,4], [5,5], [6,6]\}$

$B = \{[1,1], [1,3], [1,5], [3,1], [3,3], [3,5], [5,1], [5,3], [5,5]\}$

$A \cap B = \{[1,1], [3,3], [5,5]\}$

... if you didn't know that, read the bit in the box.

You know: $A \cup B = A + B - A \cap B$

$\Rightarrow n(A \cup B) = n(A) + n(B) - n(A \cap B) = 6 + 9 - 3 = 12$

So, $P(A \cup B) = \dfrac{n(A \cup B)}{n(S)} = \dfrac{12}{36} = \dfrac{1}{3}$

Probability... All my troubles seemed so far away...

The main thing to remember with probability is that it's actually quite *easy*. It's pretty intuitive stuff — you can get a feel
for how likely certain things are to happen, using common sense. So something like "P(A) = ½" just means "There's a
50-50 chance that A will happen". The tricky bit is using and understanding the notation. The rest's dead simple.

Probability

I think it's time you learnt the laws of nature... I mean probability. Well, it's nearly the same thing.

P(not A) = P (A') = 1 – P(A)

EXAMPLE:

I've got a mixed bag of socks, and I pick out two of them at random.

The probability of me picking out a matching pair of socks is 0.14. What is the probability of me picking out an odd pair?

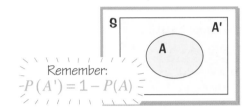

Remember:
$P(A') = 1 - P(A)$

Well, this might look a bit hard — they've hardly told you anything. But it's dead easy...

S contains all possible outcomes, so: $P(S) = 1$

The subset A contains all occurrences of a matching pair of socks, and you know: $P(A) = 0.14$

A' is the set of all outcomes that aren't in A, but are in S. So you can see that:

$$A + A' = S$$
$$\Rightarrow P(A) + P(A') = P(S)$$
$$\Rightarrow 0.14 + P(A') = 1$$
$$\Rightarrow P(A') = 0.86$$

Mutually Exclusive Events — there's No Overlap

Two events are mutually exclusive if there is no 'overlap', i.e. the events can't *both* happen — you can only have one or the other.

Formally, that's: $P(A \cup B) = P(A) + P(B)$

       or: $P(A \cap B) = 0$

EXAMPLE:

Event A = Drawing a heart out of a pack of cards
Event B = Drawing a black card out of a pack of cards
Are the two events A and B mutually exclusive?

No problem. All you need to do is find out whether $P(A \cap B) = 0$.

A = the whole suit of hearts

B = the whole suit of clubs and the whole suit of spades

If I pick out a card at random, it can't satisfy both A and B.

So $P(A \cap B) = 0$ — which means <u>A and B are mutually exclusive</u>.

Exhaustive Events Cover Everything

There's not much to this — if A and B are <u>exhaustive</u>, then all the outcomes are either in A or in B. In other words, $P(A \cup B) = 1$.

EXAMPLE:

I have a standard pack of 52 playing cards and I pick one out. What is the probability it will be either red or black?

All playing cards are either red or black, so:
$P(A \cup B) = P(S) = 1$

Probability Laws

The probability of a <u>random</u> event A happening is: $P(A) = \dfrac{n(A)}{n(S)}$

The probability of <u>either</u> A or B happening is: $P(A \cup B) = \dfrac{n(A \cup B)}{n(S)}$

The probability of <u>both</u> A and B happening is: $P(A \cap B) = \dfrac{n(A \cap B)}{n(S)}$

The probability of event A <u>NOT</u> happening is: $P(A') = 1 - P(A)$

Events A and B are <u>mutually exclusive</u> if: $P(A \cup B) = P(A) + P(B)$ (i.e. if $P(A \cap B) = 0$)

Events A and B are <u>exhaustive</u> if: $P(A \cup B) = 1$

You can't get me, I'm part of the union...

Phew. Asleep yet? I am.

zzzzzzzzzzzzzzzzzzzzzzzzzzzzzzzzzzzzzzzzzzz...   zzzzzzzzzzzzzzzzzzzzzzzzzzzzzzzzzzzzzzzzzzzz...   zzzzzzzzzzzzzzzzzzzzzzzzzzzzz...

... wha? Oh, yeah... remember that all the probabilities add up to 1. ...   ...   Can I go back to sleep now?

Tree Diagrams

Trees are great. Much better than Maths. But you're not doing A-Level Trees, so you'd better get on with this.
I guess tree diagrams are pretty cool, really. They're easy to follow, so you can quickly spot if you've gone wrong.

With Two or More Events, Draw Yourself a Tree Diagram

You use tree diagrams when you have more than one event, and loads of different possibilities.

EXAMPLE:

A regular holidaymaker in Betws-y-Coed has worked out that the probability of the sun shining is $\frac{9}{10}$ if it was sunny the previous day and $\frac{3}{10}$ if it wasn't sunny the previous day. She is on holiday from Saturday to Tuesday. If it's sunny on Saturday, what is the probability it'll be sunny the whole time she's there?

Start by drawing a tree diagram...

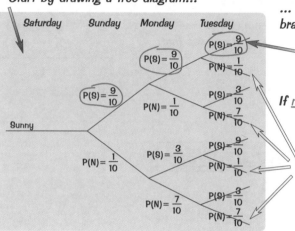

... then you can <u>multiply</u> along the branches to get the combined probabilities.

$$P(SSS) = \frac{9}{10} \times \frac{9}{10} \times \frac{9}{10} = \frac{729}{1000}$$

If <u>more than one outcome</u> is OK, you <u>add up</u> these end probabilities.

> **What is the probability it won't be sunny on Tuesday?**

These are the outcomes you need — where it's not sunny on Tuesday. So, multiply along the branches again, to get:

$$P(SSN) = \frac{9}{10} \times \frac{9}{10} \times \frac{1}{10} = \frac{81}{1000} \qquad P(NSN) = \frac{1}{10} \times \frac{3}{10} \times \frac{1}{10} = \frac{3}{1000}$$

$$P(SNN) = \frac{9}{10} \times \frac{1}{10} \times \frac{7}{10} = \frac{63}{1000} \qquad P(NNN) = \frac{1}{10} \times \frac{7}{10} \times \frac{7}{10} = \frac{49}{1000}$$

Then add them all together to allow for any of the possibilities:

$$P(A) = \frac{81}{1000} + \frac{63}{1000} + \frac{3}{1000} + \frac{49}{1000} = \frac{196}{1000} = \frac{49}{250}$$

Some Branches can Stop Before the End

Tree diagrams don't have to be symmetrical. If an event happens that makes later events <u>impossible</u>, the branch <u>stops</u>.

EXAMPLE: Simon is walking home from Buffers nightclub. The first time he walks past a ditch, the probability of him falling in is 0.7. If he successfully walks past any ditch without falling in, the probability of him falling in the next ditch is 0.1. If he falls in a ditch, he will stay there until morning. If there are three ditches, find the probability of Simon waking up in a ditch.

First draw the tree diagram.

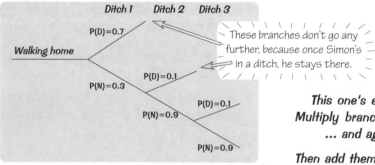

These branches don't go any further, because once Simon's in a ditch, he stays there.

The outcomes you want are: D, ND and NND.
So, find the probabilities of each of those, then add them together.

This one's easy: $\quad P(D) = 0.7$
Multiply branches: $\quad P(ND) = 0.3 \times 0.1 = 0.03$
... and again: $\quad P(NND) = 0.3 \times 0.9 \times 0.1 = 0.027$
Then add them up: $\quad P(D, ND, NND) = 0.7 + 0.03 + 0.027 = 0.757$

So the probability of Simon waking up in a ditch is 0.757.

No. 1 — The Larch...

The rules to remember are: AND = MULTIPLY and OR = ADD. <u>Don't</u> get that bit confused or you'll make a pig's ear of the whole thing. Tree diagrams really do make life easier — they help you separate all the possible outcomes and help you get the whole thing much clearer in your head. Well, I like tree diagrams anyway, but then I do prefer the easy life.

Conditional Probability

There's nothing like a good tree diagram. Not on this page, anyway. Well, maybe just the one.
But apart from that, it's just pure, unadulterated conditional probability...

$P(A \mid B)$ is 'the Probability of A, given B'

Conditional probability is when you need to find out the probability of one event occurring,
given that another related event has already occurred. And very exciting it is too.

You can find the conditional probability of A happening, given that B has already
happened, using:

$$P(A|B) = \frac{P(A \cap B)}{P(B)}$$

The probability of both A and B happening...

... divided by the probability of B happening, since we already know that's happened.

Remember this notation — they might not tell you it's a conditional probability question.

If you've got a tree diagram, the conditional probability is the probability on the second branch.

EVENT B   EVENT A

You know that B has already happened, so this is actually P(A|B).

P(B)=0.4   P(A)=0.3
              P(Not A)=0.7

P(Not B)=0.6 P(A)=0.8
              P(Not A)=0.2

EXAMPLE:

I have a box of Hallowe'en biscuits. There are five witches, three bats, three
skeletons and one Chris Tarrant. I pick out a biscuit and it's not a witch.
What's the probability that it will be a Chris Tarrant, given that it isn't a witch?

I'll give you three guesses which formula you can use for this bit.

Start by working out P(B), the probability
of the biscuit not being a witch: $P(B) = \frac{7}{12}$

Then $P(A \cap B)$ is the probability of picking
out Chris Tarrant (which satisfies B as well,
because Chris Tarrant isn't a witch...): $P(A \cap B) = \frac{1}{12}$

Which means the probability of it being Chris Tarrant, given that it's not a witch, is: $P(A|B) = \frac{\frac{1}{12}}{\frac{7}{12}} = \frac{1}{7}$

BY THE WAY:

You might well have noticed that this example would be much easier
to do by just spotting that if it isn't a witch, it being Chris Tarrant
is just one of 7 possible outcomes, instead of 12. But in some exam
questions, you might only be told the probabilities — in which case
it's easier to just stick them in the formula and away you go.

If you think about it in words, it makes sense:
"The probability of A and B is the probability of
A given B multiplied by the probability of B".

OH, AND ONE MORE THING:

This relation can be written the other way round:

... and it's the same with A and B swapped round:

$$P(A \cap B) = P(A|B) \times P(B)$$
$$= P(B|A) \times P(A)$$

(This is called the Multiplication Law, if anyone asks you.)

If $P(A \mid B) = P(A)$ then A and B are Independent Events

Ready for the ride of a lifetime? OK, here goes...

If A and B are independent, then:

$P(A|B) = P(A)$ ... and you know that: $P(A|B) = \frac{P(A \cap B)}{P(B)}$ ... so: $P(A \cap B) = P(A) \times P(B)$

EXAMPLE:

I roll one dice and pick one card out of a pack of playing cards.
What's the probability of me rolling a 1 and picking a spade?

This is true for any pair of independent events.

These two events are independent, so: $P(A \cap B) = P(A) \times P(B)$

Let event A be rolling a 1. Then: $P(A) = \frac{1}{6}$. Let event B be picking a spade. Then: $P(B) = \frac{13}{52} = \frac{1}{4}$.

So: $P(A \cap B) = P(A) \times P(B) = \frac{1}{6} \times \frac{1}{4} = \frac{1}{24}$

The best page in the world... probably

A long long time ago... I can still remember how that maths used to make me smile. And I knew if I had my chance,
that I could make those people do maths, and maybe they'd be happy for a while. But probability made me shiver... with
every tree diagram I delivered. The bad news on the doorstep — I couldn't take one more step. I can't remember if I
cried when I read about its widowed bride. Something touched me deep inside... the day the maths died.

Probability Distributions

These aren't too bad. Not really. Don't get me wrong — I'm not saying they're more fun than eating an enormous slice o apricot crumble with loads of custard on top. Only that they're not too hard to get your head round. Mmmm, crumble.

A Probability Distribution *is like a list of probabilities*

A random variable is something whose value isn't fixed — it takes on different values with different probabilities. The list of the possible values, along with their probabilities, is a <u>probability distribution</u>.

EXAMPLE:

Random variables are usually written as capital letters: X, Y etc. The random variable X could be the number of heads you get when you toss two coins.

> *Then X can take three values: 0, 1 and 2, and the probabilities of these outcomes (X=0, 1 or 2) are:*
> $P(X = 0) = 0.25$; $P(X = 1) = 0.5$; $P(X = 2) = 0.25$.

The values that these random variables can take are usually written as small letters: x_1, x_2, x_3, etc.

> *With the two coins example, X (the random variable) is the number of heads you get — it changes each time you toss the coins.*
> *The possible outcomes are $x_1 = 0$, $x_2 = 1$, $x_3 = 2$.*

The probabilities of X taking any of these values are often written as p_1, p_2, p_3 etc.

> $P(X = 0) = P(X = x_1) = p_1$
> $P(X = 1) = P(X = x_2) = p_2$
> $P(X = 2) = P(X = x_3) = p_3$

So p_1 is the probability that $X = x_1$, where $x_1 = 0$. And likewise for p_2 and p_3.

And since X must take one of these values, when you add all the probabilities together, you get 1.

This 'sigma' just means you're adding all the different p's together.

$$\sum p_i = p_1 + p_2 + p_3 = 0.25 + 0.5 + 0.25$$
$$= 1$$

A Probability Density Function *(p.d.f.) gives probabilities*

Quite often, the probability distribution is given using a function — these are called <u>probability density functions</u> (which is sometimes abbreviated to <u>p.d.f.</u>).

EXAMPLE:

The p.d.f. of the random variable X is: $P(X = x) = k(10 - x)$, for x = 1, 2, 4 and 8. Find the value of the constant k.

You put a possible value of X in a p.d.f., and the p.d.f. tells you the probability that X will take that value.

> *You know that X can take the values 1, 2, 4 and 8 — call these values x_1, x_2, x_3 and x_4 (or even just x_i for i=1, 2, 3 and 4). Now work out the probability of X taking any of these values using the p.d.f.*
>
> *x_1, x_2, x_3 and x_4 are the possible values that X can take.*
>
> | x_i | $p_i = P(X = x_i)$ $=k(10-x_i)$ |
> |---|---|
> | $x_1 = 1$ | $p_1 = k(10 - 1) = 9k$ |
> | $x_2 = 2$ | $p_2 = k(10 - 2) = 8k$ |
> | $x_3 = 4$ | $p_3 = k(10 - 4) = 6k$ |
> | $x_4 = 8$ | $p_4 = k(10 - 8) = 2k$ |
>
> *p_1, p_2, p_3 and p_4 are the probabilities of X taking the values x_1, x_2, x_3 and x_4. Work them out using the p.d.f.*
>
> *These probabilities have to add up to 1, so...*
>
> $$\sum p_i = 9k + 8k + 6k + 2k = 25k$$
> $$= 1$$
>
> *$\sum p_i = 1$ is always true.*
>
> *So k must be $\frac{1}{25}$.*

Remember: Britney Spears likes doing probability questions...

It's true. She can't get enough of them after doing a show. She's often to be heard wandering around backstage shouting, "I'm a star, and I want to do probability questions — SO GET ME SOME PROBABILITY QUESTIONS". Yep, stars can be like that. Anyway, just remember that these random variables aren't fixed — they take different values.

Expected Values and Variances

When you know a probability distribution (say, the probabilities of getting the numbers 1 – 6 when you throw a dice), you can work out what value you'd expect to get on average, if you kept on throwing the dice for long enough...

The Mean of a random variable is the same as the Expected Value

$$Expected\ value,\ E(X) = \sum x_i\, P(X = x_i) = \sum x_i p_i$$

Just multiply each possible value by its probability, and add up the results.

EXAMPLE:

Right then, I've got this dice, and my friend's bet me £1 000 000 that I can't get a mean score of 4 or more after 10 000 throws. I reckon the odds are pretty good, though. And I'll prove it...

Let X be a random variable which takes the values 1, 2, 3, 4, 5 and 6 with equal probability. Then the values of x_i and p_i are:

Before trying to use this formula, it's a good idea to write down all the x's and the p's.

$$x_1 = 1;\ x_2 = 2;\ x_3 = 3;\ x_4 = 4;\ x_5 = 5;\ x_6 = 6.$$

$$p_1 = p_2 = p_3 = p_4 = p_5 = p_6 = \tfrac{1}{6}$$

The probability of getting any of these numbers is 1/6 — since all the probabilities must add up to 1.

So if you put these in the formula, you get...

$$E(X) = \sum_{all\ x_i} x_i p_i = \left(1 \times \tfrac{1}{6}\right) + \left(2 \times \tfrac{1}{6}\right) + \left(3 \times \tfrac{1}{6}\right) + \left(4 \times \tfrac{1}{6}\right) + \left(5 \times \tfrac{1}{6}\right) + \left(6 \times \tfrac{1}{6}\right)$$

$$= \tfrac{1}{6}(1 + 2 + 3 + 4 + 5 + 6) = \tfrac{21}{6} = \tfrac{7}{2} = 3.5$$

So I'd expect my mean score to end up close to 3.5. Oh dear. Oh dear, oh dear.

This doesn't mean you'd expect your average score to be exactly 3.5 — only that you'd be surprised if it wasn't pretty close to that after a while.

And as you take more throws, the closer your average score will get to 3.5.

Work out the Variance — go on, you know you want to...

The expected value is what the mean of your observations of a random variable will approach as you keep throwing dice, tossing coins etc.. And in the same way, you can also work out what the variance will get closer to.

$$Var(X) = E(X^2) - [E(X)]^2 = \sum x_i^2 p_i - \left(\sum x_i p_i\right)^2$$

This first bit must be $E(X^2)$... *...because this last bracket is $[E(X)]^2$.*

EXAMPLE:

Using the same dice-throwing example as above, work out the variance of the random variable X.

① First you need $E(X^2) = \sum x_i^2 p_i$.

Instead of using the values 1, 2, 3, 4, 5 and 6 in the expected value formula, use 1, 4, 9, 16, 25 and 36. This'll give you the expected value of X^2.

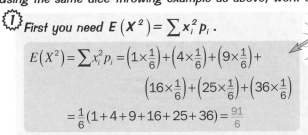

$$E(X^2) = \sum x_i^2 p_i = \left(1 \times \tfrac{1}{6}\right) + \left(4 \times \tfrac{1}{6}\right) + \left(9 \times \tfrac{1}{6}\right) +$$

$$\left(16 \times \tfrac{1}{6}\right) + \left(25 \times \tfrac{1}{6}\right) + \left(36 \times \tfrac{1}{6}\right)$$

$$= \tfrac{1}{6}(1 + 4 + 9 + 16 + 25 + 36) = \tfrac{91}{6}$$

② Then the variance is just given by:

$$Var(X) = E(X^2) - [E(X)]^2$$

$$= \tfrac{91}{6} - \left(\tfrac{7}{2}\right)^2 = \tfrac{91}{6} - \tfrac{49}{4} = \tfrac{182 - 147}{12} = \tfrac{35}{12}$$

Transformed Random Variables

If you define a new random variable $Y = aX + b$, then the values of $E(Y)$ and $Var(Y)$ follow some pretty simple rules:

(i) $E(Y) = aE(X) + b$,

(ii) $Var(Y) = a^2 Var(X)$.

EXAMPLE: Say you've already found out that E(X) = 5 and Var(X) = 1.5.
You're told Y = 3X + 4, so: E(Y) = 3E(X) + 4 = 19
and: Var(Y) = 9Var(X) = 13.5

Yeah don't worry, I don't understand this either — no one does...

Some of this stuff is a bit tricky to get your head round. The mean of a random variable (which is the same as the expected value) is a number, and it never changes, because it doesn't depend on observations. Like the mean of the random variable in the first part of this page was 3.5. And the mean of this random variable will always be exactly 3.5. But that's not to say that you'd expect the mean of 10 000 observations to be exactly 3.5. It'll certainly be pretty close, but might not be spot on — because observations are real life, and the expected value is theory. If this doesn't seem to make any sense, don't worry too much — because they won't ask you a question on it. But it might make some tricky bits a bit clearer.

Histograms and Stem & Leaf Diagrams

To make data 'useful', you need to organise it in some way. A good way is to draw a picture — well, a graph, anyway.

Histograms **are glorified bar charts**

Group 1 were timed to see how many minutes it took each of the 25 students to do a maths problem. The results were:

5, 6, 10, 11, 14, 15, 17, 17, 18, 18, 19, 21, 21, 21, 22, 24, 24, 26, 27, 28, 29, 31, 34, 34, 39.

The first thing to do is gather the results together in a table, showing the <u>frequency distribution</u>.

These are the classes, each class width is 5 minutes.

When something falls on a class boundary (like 5 and 10 here), put them in the bigger class. (So 5 goes in the 5-10 class, and 10 goes in 10-15.)

Time in minutes	0-5	5-10	10-15	15-20	20-25	25-30	30-35	35-40	Total
Frequency	0	2	3	6	6	4	3	1	25

To make the results easier to understand quickly, you could make a histogram. There are two ways to do this.

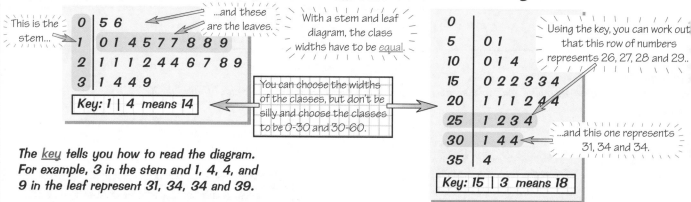

A Use <u>equal</u> class widths:

B Use <u>unequal</u> class widths — but you need to work out the <u>frequency density</u> of each class first:

Time in minutes	0-15	15-20	20-25	25-30	30-40	Total
Frequency	5	6	6	4	4	25
Class width	15	5	5	5	10	
Frequency density (=Frequency ÷ class width)	$\frac{1}{3}$	$\frac{6}{5}$	$\frac{6}{5}$	$\frac{4}{5}$	$\frac{2}{5}$	

There aren't many observations in the first three classes, so group them together. And the same goes for the last two classes.

Make an extra row in your table for the frequency densities.

Now it's the <u>area</u> of each bar that shows the frequency — not the <u>height</u>.

Stem and Leaf **diagrams use the actual data**

A <u>stem and leaf</u> diagram is a bit like a histogram, but the data itself is used to make the diagram.

This is the stem...

...and these are the leaves.

```
0 | 5 6
1 | 0 1 4 5 7 7 8 8 9
2 | 1 1 1 2 4 4 6 7 8 9
3 | 1 4 4 9
Key: 1 | 4 means 14
```

With a stem and leaf diagram, the class widths have to be <u>equal</u>.

You can choose the widths of the classes, but don't be silly and choose the classes to be 0-30 and 30-60.

```
 0 |
 5 | 0 1
10 | 0 1 4
15 | 0 2 2 3 3 4
20 | 1 1 1 2 4 4
25 | 1 2 3 4
30 | 1 4 4
35 | 4
Key: 15 | 3 means 18
```

Using the key, you can work out that this row of numbers represents 26, 27, 28 and 29..

...and this one represents 31, 34 and 34.

The <u>key</u> tells you how to read the diagram. For example, 3 in the stem and 1, 4, 4, and 9 in the leaf represent 31, 34, 34 and 39.

You can do these Back-to-Back...

If you've got two sets of data that you want to compare, you can do <u>back-to-back</u> stem and leaf diagrams.
Another group of students (Group 2) solved the same problem in the following times (in minutes):

3, 3, 3, 5, 8, 8, 9, 12, 13, 14, 14, 18, 18, 19, 20, 22, 22, 24.

So the two stem and leaf diagrams back to back would look like this...

Group 2		Group 1
3 3 3 5 8 8 9	0	5 6
2 3 4 4 8 8 9	1	0 1 4 5 7 7 8 8 9
0 2 2 4	2	1 1 1 2 4 4 6 7 8 9
	3	1 4 4 9

Key: (Group 1) 1 | 4 means 14,
(Group 2) 8 | 1 means 18.

It looks like the students in Group 2 were better, but it's difficult to say for sure — perhaps their teacher gave them more help.

You need an extra key for Group 2 because the graph is 'backwards'.

Histograms — not what Tiggers like best...

Histograms where the classes are different widths are useful when some of the classes have really high frequencies and some have very few. So group enough of the smaller values together until you've got a sensible looking histogram. And don't forget to label any graphs that you draw — label the axes and the whole graph, so it's clear what it's all about.

Cows

The stuff on this page isn't strictly on the syllabus. But I've included it anyway because I reckon it's really important stuff that you ought to know.

There are loads of Different Types of Cows

DAIRY CATTLE

Every day a dairy cow can produce up to 128 pints of milk — which can be used to make 14 lbs of cheese, 5 gallons of ice cream, or 6 lbs butter.

The Jersey
The Jersey is a small breed best suited to pastures in high rainfall areas. It is kept for its creamy milk.

<u>Advantages</u>
1) Can produce creamy milk until old age.
2) Milk is the highest in fat of any dairy breed (5.2%).
3) Fairly docile, although bulls can't be trusted.

<u>Disadvantages</u>
1) Produces less milk than most other breeds.

The Holstein-Friesian
This breed can be found in many areas. It is kept mainly for milk.

<u>Advantages</u>
1) Produce more milk than any breed.
2) The breed is large, so bulls can be sold for beef.

<u>Disadvantages</u>
1) Milk is low in fat (3.5%).

BEEF CATTLE

Cows are sedentary animals who spend up to 8 hours a day chewing the cud while standing still or lying down to rest after grazing. Getting fat for people to eat.

The Angus
The Angus is best suited to areas where there is moderately high rainfall.

<u>Advantages</u>
1) Early maturing.
2) High ratio of meat to body weight.
3) Forages well.
4) Adaptable.

The Hereford
The Hereford matures fairly early, but later than most shorthorn breeds. All Herefords have white faces, and if a Hereford is crossbred with any other breed of cow, all the offspring will have white or partially white faces.

<u>Advantages</u>
1) Hardy.
2) Adaptable to different feeds.

<u>Disadvantages</u>
1) Susceptible to eye diseases.

Milk comes from Cows

This is <u>really</u> important — try not to forget it.

Milk is an emulsion of butterfat suspended in a solution of water (roughly 80%), lactose, proteins and salts. Cow's milk has a specific gravity around 1.03.
It's pasteurised by heating it to 63° C for 30 minutes. It's then rapidly cooled and stored below 10° C .

Louis Pasteur began his experiments into 'pasteurisation' in 1856. By 1946, the vacuum pasteurisation method had been perfected, and in 1948, UHT (ultra heat-treated) pasteurisation was introduced.

$$cow + grass = fat\ cow$$
$$fat\ cow + milking\ machine \Rightarrow milk$$

You will often see cows with pieces of grass sticking out of their mouths.

SOME IMPORTANT FACTS TO REMEMBER:
• A newborn calf can walk on its own an hour after birth
• A cow's teeth are only on the bottom of her mouth
• While some cows can live up to 40 years, they generally don't live beyond 20.

Cows on the Internet

For more information on cows, try these websites:

www.allcows.com (including Cow of the Month)
www.crazyforcows.com (with cow e-postcards)
www.moomilk.com (includes a 'What's the cow thinking?' contest.)
http://www.geocities.com/Hollywood/9317/meowcow.html
(for cow-tipping on the Internet)

The Cow
The cow is of the bovine ilk;
One end is moo, the other, milk.

— Ogden Nash

Famous Cows and Cow Songs

FAMOUS COWS
1) Ermintrude from the Magic Roundabout.
2) Graham Heifer — the Boddingtons cow.
3) Other TV commercial cows — Anchor, Dairylea
4) The cow that jumped over the moon.
5) Greek Mythology was full of gods turning themselves and their girlfriends into cattle.

COWS IN POP MUSIC
1) Size of a Cow — the Wonder Stuff
2) Saturday Night at the Moo-vies — The Drifters
3) What can I do to make you milk me? — The Cows
4) One to an-udder — the Charlatans
5) Milk me baby, one more time — Britney Spears

Where's me Jersey — I'm Friesian...

Cow-milking — an underrated skill, in my opinion. As Shakespeare once wrote, 'Those who can milk cows are likely to get pretty good grades in maths exams, no word of a lie'. Well, he probably would've written something like that if he was into cows. And he would've written it because cows are helpful when you're trying to work out what a question's all about — and once you know that, you can decide the best way forward. And if you don't believe me, remember the saying of the ancient Roman Emperor Julius Caesar, 'If in doubt, draw a cow'.

Mean, Mode and Median

The three M's — they're all types of _average_. Which means that they all give some idea of where the data is 'centred'.

The Mean is the normal average

When people say the 'average', they usually mean the _mean_. You know how to find it...

$$\overline{x} = \frac{\sum x_i}{n}$$

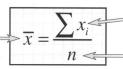

Write the mean like this — it's pronounced "x-bar".

Add up all the numbers...

...and divide by how many there are.

The $\sum x_i$ just means 'add up all the values of x'.

EXAMPLE: A town's petrol stations were asked the cost of their petrol. The results in pence per litre were:

75.1   77.3   78.1   79.1   79.1   79.1   79.3   79.8
80.2   80.2   80.4   80.9   81.3   82.1   82.6   84.3

So the mean price is just: $\dfrac{\sum x_i}{n} = \dfrac{75.1 + 77.3 + ... + 84.3}{16} = 79.9p$

This bit on the top of the fraction is just $\sum x_i$ — it's all the values of x added together.

...and in a Frequency Table...

$$\overline{x} = \frac{\sum f_i x_i}{\sum f_i} \qquad i = 1, ..., n$$

Here, n is the number of _classes_, f_i is the number of data values in that class (the frequency), and x_i is the mid-class value.

EXAMPLE:

Sometimes, data's given in a _frequency table_, where each item's put into one of several _classes_. This means you don't know any prices exactly. But the frequencies f_i tell you how many petrol stations sell petrol in each of these price classe

Pence per litre	75 - 77	77 - 79	79 - 80	80 - 81	81 - 82	82 - 84	84 - 88	Total
Frequency, f_i	1	2	5	4	1	2	1	16

You only know roughly how much petrol cost in these petrol stations.

What you have to do is assume that all the petrol stations selling petrol for between 79 and 80 pence were selling it for exactly 79.5p — i.e. you use the _mid-class value_ of each class.

Add a row to your table with the mid-class values...

...and another containing the mid-class values multiplied by the frequencies.

Pence per litre	75 - 77	77 - 79	79 - 80	80 - 81	81 - 82	82 - 84	84 - 88	Total
Mid-class value, x_i	76	78	79.5	80.5	81.5	83	86	
Frequency, f_i	1	2	5	4	1	2	1	16
$f_i x_i$	76	156	397.5	322	81.5	166	86	1285

This is the bottom lir of the mean formula.

...and this is the top line.

So the mean price of a litre of petrol is $\frac{1285}{16} = 80.3p$.

A different answer — this can happen when you have to estimate (i.e. guess) some values.

This method works because if the two prices between 77 and 79 were 77.4 and 78.8, then these values would contribute 77.4 + 78.8 = 156.2 to the total of the prices. Using the midpoint value and multiplying by the frequency means you're approximating this to 2 × 78 = 156.

The Mode is the one that occurs most often

This one's easy. Just count up how often each number appears and the _mode_ is the one that happens most often.

EXAMPLES:

For the petrol data, the value that occurs most often is 79.1p (occurring three times) — so that's the _mode_ (or the _modal value_).

When you only have the data in a frequency table, you can only say the _modal class_ — i.e. the class that occurs with the highest frequency.
Here, the modal class is the class 79 – 80p .

Sometimes you get two or more modal values — just write them all down. DON'T find their mean.

Sing along — tables, tables, tables, tables, tables, tables are grea

The mean's the most common type of average, but it's easily affected by one very big or one very small value. If a garage was ripping people off and charging £1.30 for a litre, then the mean would be very different because of just one value (so it doesn't always give the best overall picture). And write down the tables — don't do these in your head.

Section Five — Probability and Statistics

Mean, Mode and Median

The median's another average, but it's a bit more fiddly to work out sometimes. Basically, you line up all the figures in order, and choose the one in the middle. And who said maths wasn't a thrill a minute...

The Median is the value in the Middle

Arrange the data in order of size and the <u>median</u> is the $\frac{1}{2}(n+1)^{th}$ value.

EXAMPLE: Thirteen people work for Catcham and Cheetham, a small firm of solicitors in southern England. Their weekly wages (in £) are as follows:

1308 346 288 385 442 288 250 337 423 481 375 1058 288

To find the median of 13 values, you need the $\frac{1}{2}(13+1)^{th} = \frac{1}{2}(14)^{th} = 7^{th}$ value.

Line the wages up in order first, from smallest to biggest...

...and the median is the one in the middle.

250 288 288 288 337 346 **375** 385 423 442 481 1058 1308

So the median wage is £375 per week.

There are six values smaller than the median...

...and six values bigger than the median.

EXAMPLE: Another solicitor, Mr Scarper, joins the firm, so the wages in order are now:

The median is here — then there are seven wages higher than this and seven lower.

250 288 288 288 337 346 **375 385** 423 442 481 1058 1204 1308

To get the median, find the <u>mean</u> of these two.

With 14 values, the median is the $\frac{1}{2}(14+1)^{th} = \frac{1}{2}(15)^{th} = 7\frac{1}{2}^{th}$ value — just use the mean of the 7th and 8th values.

So the median wage is $\frac{375+385}{2} = £380$ per week.

And you can also do it when you've got a Frequency Table...

EXAMPLE:

A census of all the law firms in a medium sized town found that the wages of the staff were as follows:

Wages (in thousands of £)	15-20	20-25	25-30	30-35	35-40	40-50	Total
Frequency	18	35	17	9	5	4	88

Here, n = 88. So $\frac{1}{2}(n+1) = \frac{1}{2}(88+1) = 44\frac{1}{2}$.

The median is the $44\frac{1}{2}^{th}$ smallest (or $44\frac{1}{2}^{th}$ biggest) value — and this occurs somewhere in the 20 - 25 group. But there are 18 values in the 15 - 20 class, so you need the $26\frac{1}{2}^{th}$ value $(=44\frac{1}{2} - 18)$ from the 20 - 25 group.

There are 35 readings in the 20 - 25 interval, so break the interval down into 35 equal parts of width $^5/_{35}$ (since the interval is 5 units wide), and assume there's a reading at each of these new points...

This is called <u>linear interpolation</u>.

$20+\frac{5}{35}$ $20+\left(2\times\frac{5}{35}\right)$ $25-\frac{5}{35}$

...and take the reading that would be 26½ units along.

It'll be at $20 + (26\frac{1}{2} \times \frac{5}{35}) = 23.8$.

So the median wage is approximately £24 000.

You can only give a rough answer here, because you've assumed the readings are equally spaced out — which in reality they might not be.

If music be the food of maths, play on Rembrandt...

The median's not so easily affected by one very big or very small value — so it's sometimes better to use that, rather than the mean. Another thing that's important here is the business of <u>linear interpolation</u>. It just means assuming that all your readings are equally spaced out, which they may or may not be in real life. It just helps to make things easier.

Cumulative Frequency Diagrams

Another way to summarise the data is using a cumulative frequency diagram. You need an extra line or two in your tables

The Cumulative Frequency is a Running Total

The cumulative frequency is the number of observations up to a particular amount.

The cumulative percentage frequency is the percentage of observations up to a particular amount.

EXAMPLE: The weights of marrows in the villages of Nutmeg and Shrewton are summarised below...

Weight of marrow (in kg)	0 - 0.5	0.6 - 1.0	1.1 - 1.5	1.6 - 2.0	2.1 - 3.0	3.1 - 4.0	Total
Frequency (Nutmeg)	1	4	5	8	5	1	24
Frequency (Shrewton)	0	2	3	8	8	5	26

The classes here have 'gaps' between them — the first class ends at 0.5 kg and the second starts at 0.6 kg.

Anything less than 0.55 kg would be in the first class, anything from 0.55 kg up to 1.05 kg will be in the second class, and so on.

So the upper class boundaries of the first two classes are 0.55 kg and 1.05 kg.

Make the cumulative frequency tables by taking the upper class boundary of each class and working out how many marrows weigh this or less.

Weight of marrow (in kg)	0.55	1.05	1.55	2.05	3.05	4.05
Cumulative frequency (Nutmeg)	1	5	10	18	23	24
Cumulative % frequency (Nutmeg)	4.2	20.8	41.7	75	95.8	100
Cumulative frequency (Shrewton)	0	2	5	13	21	26
Cumulative % frequency (Shrewton)	0	7.7	19.2	50	80.8	100

Divide the cumulative frequency by the total number of marrows in each village, and multiply by 100.

To draw a cumulative frequency graph, plot the cumulative frequencies against the weights.

You can join the points with straight lines or a curve — it doesn't matter.

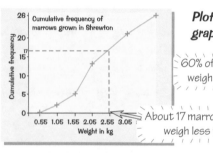

About 17 marrows in Shrewton weigh less than 2.5 kg.

Plot a cumulative % graph in the same way.

60% of the marrows in Nutmeg weigh less than about 1.8 kg.

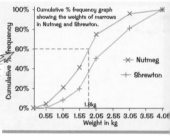

The Quartiles divide the data into four

It's dead easy to find the median and the quartiles from a cumulative percentage frequency graph.

1) The median splits the data in two — 50% of the marrows weigh more than the median and 50% weigh less.

2) The quartiles are similar, but along with the median they split the data into four, so 25% of the marrows weigh less than the lower quartile, and 75% weigh less than the upper quartile.

Just read the median and the quartiles from the graph by finding 50% (for the median), and 25% and 75% (for the quartiles) on the vertical axis, and finding the corresponding values on the horizontal axis.

The interquartile range is the distance between the upper and lower quartiles. Here, the interquartile range is 2.0 – 1.1 = 0.9 kg.

This is the lower quartile. This is the median. This is the upper quartile.

Box and Whisker diagrams

A box and whisker diagram shows how spread out the data is in an easy to understand way. It's a good idea to do them underneath a cumulative % frequency graph.

The lines on the end of the box stretch as far as the maximum and minimum values.

The ends of the box show the upper and lower quartiles.

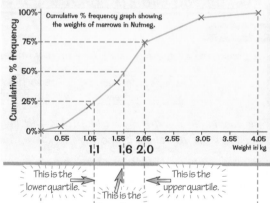

The line through the middle of the box shows the median.

What have I... What have I... What have I done to deserve this...

Despite what you're thinking, this page isn't too bad. The big ideas are upper class boundaries and cumulative frequencies. For the upper class boundaries, always ask yourself how big something could be and still make it into each class. Then use those figures on your cumulative frequency graphs. And yes, it is too late to change your mind and do French instead.

Measures of Spread

There are quite a few different ways to measure how 'spread out' data is. Get a load of all this nonsense...

The Range is the difference between the Smallest and the Biggest

The range is easy to find — just take the smallest value from the biggest value.

$$\text{Range} = \text{biggest} - \text{smallest}$$

EXAMPLE:

The five companies on a trading estate were asked how many people they employed. The results were:

19, 11, 25, 27 and 24.

The smallest value here is 11 and the biggest is 27, so the range is given by: Range = 27 – 11 = 16.

The Variance is really jolly important

$$\text{Variance, } s^2 = \frac{1}{n}\sum (x_i - \overline{x})^2 = \frac{1}{n}\sum x_i^2 - \overline{x}^2$$

Think of this as the average of the squares minus the square of the average.

Think of this as the mean of the squared deviations from the mean.

The variance is a dead important measure of how spread out data is. Sadly, it's a pain to work out. Time for more tables.

You can do it this way...

x_i	Deviation from mean = $x_i - \overline{x}$	Square of deviation = $(x_i - \overline{x})^2$
19	-2.2	4.84
11	-10.2	104.04
25	3.8	14.44
27	5.8	33.64
24	2.8	7.84
Total 106		164.80
Mean 21.2		32.96

So the variance is 32.96.

It doesn't matter that the data is in columns this time, rather than rows.

The variance is the mean of these numbers, so sum this column...

...then divide by the number of values n (= 5), to find the variance.

...or you can do it this way.

x_i	x_i^2
19	361
11	121
25	625
27	729
24	576
Total 106	2412
Mean 21.2	482.4

Find the mean of these numbers, and subtract the square of the normal mean.

So the variance = $482.4 - 21.2^2 = 32.96$.

When the data's in a frequency table, use the Mid-class Values

$$\text{Variance, } s^2 = \frac{1}{n}\sum f_i(x_i - \overline{x})^2 = \frac{1}{n}\sum f_i x_i^2 - \overline{x}^2$$

With data in tables, assume all readings in a class take the mid-class value.

This data shows numbers of people employed by the firms in a town. You'll need to find the mean first.

People employed	5	10	15	20	30	50	Totals
Frequency, f_i	1	5	10	4	4	1	25
Mid-class value, x_i	2.5	7.5	12.5	17.5	25	40	
$f_i x_i$	2.5	37.5	125	70	100	40	375
						Mean	15

Divide the bottom total by the top one and you get the mean.

And then you can find the mean of the squared deviations...

Deviation = $x_i - \overline{x}$	-12.5	-7.5	-2.5	2.5	10	25	Total
$(x_i - \overline{x})^2$	156.25	56.25	6.25	6.25	100	625	
$f_i \times (x_i - \overline{x})^2$	156.25	281.25	62.5	25	400	625	1550

So the variance is $\frac{1550}{25} = 62$.

Divide this by the sum of the frequencies to find the variance.

Or you can do the 'mean of the squares minus the square of the mean' — and you should get the same answer.

Square of mid-class value, x_i^2	6.25	56.25	156.25	306.25	625	1600	Total
$x_i^2 f_i$	6.25	281.25	1562.5	1225	2500	1600	7175
						Mean	287

And so the variance is $287 - 15^2 = 62$.

So the mean of the squared mid-class values is $\frac{7175}{25} = 287$.

It's only statistics — take the pain, take the pain...

This all gets very confusing, very quickly. The only way to have any chance of avoiding a massive maths-induced mental meltdown is to draw the tables. Yep, draw the tables — it's the only way. The only way, I tell you. You can't do this without tables. Heading for a fall if you even try. Oh yes, a mighty big fall. That's what my grandpa always told me. And...

Measures of Spread

Right then — almost done with this unpleasantness. Just a couple of easy bits to go, and then you're free to run, skip, play, dance and sing. And do all the rest of that maths homework your teacher gave you...

The Standard Deviation is the square root of the variance

Easy. Once you've got the variance, all you have to do to find the standard deviation is take the **square root**.

$$\text{Standard deviation}, s = \sqrt{\text{Variance}}$$

So using the examples on the opposite page that you've just found the variances of, you can easily work out the standard deviations...

For the first example...   ...and for the second example...

> You might also see it written: $sd(x) = 7.87$ or $s_x = 7.87$. Just make it clear that you mean the standard deviation.

 $s = \sqrt{32.96} = 5.74$ *(to 2 d.p.)*   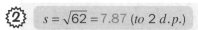 $s = \sqrt{62} = 7.87$ *(to 2 d.p.)*

Transformed variables have different Means and Variances

It can be useful to transform the data. Fortunately it's easy to work out the new mean, variance and standard deviation.

$$\text{If } y_i = ax_i + b, \text{ then}$$
$$(i) \quad \overline{y} = a\overline{x} + b$$
$$(ii) \quad s_y^2 = a^2 s_x^2$$
$$(iii) \quad s_y = as_x$$

> This is just like the stuff on page 39 — same rules apply.

> Here, s_x^2 is the *variance* of the set of x's and s_y^2 is the variance of the set of y's. So s_x and s_y are the *standard deviations*.

> If $a < 0$, you'll get a negative standard deviation. But the standard deviation can NEVER be negative, so just ignore the minus sign.

EXAMPLE:

When a dice was thrown, the following scores (x_1, x_2, ..., x_{10}) were obtained:

> 3, 4, 2, 2, 6, 1, 2, 3, 2, 5

Find the mean, variance and standard deviation of these scores. Then find the new mean, variance and standard deviation if you get 20 points for a 1, 30 points for a 2, 40 points for a 3 and so on, up to 70 points for a 6.

Using the numbers above:

(i) The mean is:
$$\overline{x} = \frac{\sum x_i}{n}$$
$$= \frac{3+4+2+2+6+1+2+3+2+5}{10} = \frac{30}{10} = 3$$

(ii) The variance is:
$$s_x^2 = \frac{\sum x_i^2}{n} - \overline{x}^2 = \frac{9+16+4+4+36+1+4+9+4+25}{10} - 3^2$$
$$= \frac{112}{10} - 9$$
$$= 11.2 - 9 = 2.2$$

> Find the mean of the squares and subtract the square of the means.

(iii) The standard deviation is:
$$s_x = \sqrt{s_x^2}$$
$$= \sqrt{2.2} = 1.48 \text{ (to 2 d.p.)}$$

The scoring system of 20 points for a 1, 30 for a 2 and so on means you can work out what new score (y_i) each of the old scores (x_i) would correspond to using this formula:

$$y_i = 10x_i + 10$$

> Finding this is like solving simultaneous equations:
> E.g. $20 = 1a + b$,
> $30 = 2a + b$.
> So $a = 10$ and $b = 10$.

So the new mean, variance and standard deviation will be given by:

(i) for the mean:
$$\overline{y} = a\overline{x} + b$$
$$= 10\overline{x} + b$$
$$= (10 \times 3) + 10 = 40$$

(ii) for the variance:
$$s_y^2 = a^2 s_x^2$$
$$= 10^2 s_x^2$$
$$= 100 \times 2.2$$
$$= 220$$

(iii) for the standard deviation:
$$s_y = as_x$$
$$= 10s_x$$
$$= 10 \times 1.48$$
$$= 14.8$$

Hmm — not very thrilling. Still — better spread than dead...

At last. At long last. You thought you'd never see another one. But here it is. Oh yes, they're finally back. A nice, easy page. Nothing too hard here. Take a square root, multiply a couple of numbers together and then add something. I can handle that. Statistics — ha, it's easy. I like it. Might even take the statistics module. That's cos I'm mad.

Section Five Revision Questions

They think it's all over...

1) Work out the probabilities of getting the following scores when rolling two dice:
a) 12   b) 9   c) 6   d) 10   e) 1

2) a) If you have two events, A and B: i) what does $A \cap B$ mean ? ii) What does $A \cup B$ mean?
b) Event A is "Picking out a jack from a standard pack of 52 cards" and event B is "Picking out a black card".
   If I pick out one card, work out the following: i) P(A) ii) P(B) iii) $P(A \cap B)$ iv) $P(A \cup B)$

3) The probability that I will go home on time tonight is 0.1. What is the probability that I WON'T go home on time?

4) I roll a dice once. Event X is "I roll an even number" and Y is "I roll an odd number".
a) Which of these statements are correct?
   A: All outcomes satisfy either X or Y   B: No outcomes satisfy either X or Y
   C: No outcomes satisfy both X and Y   D: X and Y are never satisfied with anything
b) i) Are X and Y mutually exclusive? ii) Is $X \cup Y$ exhaustive?

5) The probability of me dropping a bacon sandwich out of the window on any morning in December is 0.6. The probability of it being a windy day in December is 0.4. The probability of a dropped bacon sandwich hitting its target (my boss's shiny red MG) is 0.1 if it's a windy day and 0.8 if it's not windy. Draw a tree diagram, and hence calculate these probabilities on any day in December: (i) it being windy and me hitting my boss's shiny red MG with a bacon sandwich, (ii) it being still and me hitting my boss's shiny red MG with a bacon sandwich, iii) me hitting my boss's shiny red MG with a bacon sandwich whether or not it's windy.

6) a) If you are given $P(A \cap B)$ and P(B), how do you work out P(A|B)?
b) If P(A|B) = 0.8 and P(B) = 0.5, find $P(A \cap B)$. If P(A) = 0.6, are A and B independent events?

7) The probability distribution of a random variable X is as follows:

x	3	6	9	12
$P(X = x)$	0.2	0.4	p	0.3

Work out the value of p.

8) The p.d.f. of a random variable is $P(X = x) = k(x+3)$ for x = 2, 4, 6, 8, 10. Find the value of the constant k.

9) I have a pack of cards with 2 jokers in it. When I pick out a card, the scoring is as follows: even number = 1 pt; odd number = 4 pts; ace, king, queen or jack = 9 pts; joker = 16 pts.
Let X be the random variable which takes the values 1, 4, 9 and 16. Find the expected value and the variance of X.

10) The numbers of beans eaten by the 20 competitors in this year's One Minute Toothpick Baked Bean Eating Competition were as follows:
34, 39, 41, 49, 51, 56, 56, 56, 58, 59, 60, 61, 62, 68, 70, 78, 85, 87, 91, 97
a) Draw two histograms of these results, one using equal class widths and one using unequal class widths.
b) Draw a stem and leaf diagram to show this data, using sensible class widths.

11) Find the mode, median and mean of the results from this year's One Minute Toothpick Baked Bean Eating Competition. (Use the results from question 10.)

12) I have just baked 20 chocolate butterfly buns, and I'm measuring them all to check that they conform with EU regulation 9705F. Their diameters (in mm) are as follows:
47, 48, 49, 49, 50, 50, 50, 50, 50, 50, 51, 51, 51, 51, 52, 52, 53, 54, 54, 56
a) Draw a cumulative % frequency diagram of these results.
b) Find the median and the upper and lower quartiles.
c) Draw a box and whisker diagram underneath the cumulative frequency diagram.
d) EU regulation 9705F states that any batch of 20 butterfly buns must have a median diameter of 50 mm and an interquartile range of no more than 5 mm. Do my buns conform with 9705F?

13) Find the range, variance and standard deviation of diameters of the butterfly buns. (Use the values in question 12.)

14) The attention span of 25 A-Level Stats students was measured during a one-hour lesson on Standard Deviations. The results were as follows:

Attention span (minutes)	0 - 10	10 - 20	20 - 30	30 - 40	40 - 50	50 - 60
Frequency	3	5	9	4	3	1

Find: a) the modal class, b) the median,
c) the mean,   d) the variance,
e) the standard deviation.

15) If x_i = the length of time for which a student is concentrating, the length of time for which that student is not concentrating is given by $y_i = 60 - x_i$. Use your answers from question 13 to find for y: a) the mean, b) the variance, c) the standard deviation.

... it is now.

General Certificate of Education
Advanced Subsidiary (AS) and Advanced Level

AQA Me (Methods) — Practice Exam One

1 (i) Factorise the quadratic expression $x^2 - 2x - 63$. [2]

(ii) Hence find all the solutions to the equation $f(x) = 0$, where $f(x)$ is given by $f(x) = x^4 - 2x^2 - 63$. [2]

(iii) Find the coordinates of all the stationary points of the graph $y = f(x)$, and find the gradient at the point $x = 2$. [3]

2 (i) Write down the exact value of $36^{-\frac{1}{2}}$ [2]

(ii) Simplify $\dfrac{a^6 \times a^3}{\sqrt{a^4}} \div a^{\frac{1}{2}}$ [2]

(iii) Express $\left(5\sqrt{5} + 2\sqrt{3}\right)^2$ in the form $a + b\sqrt{c}$, where a, b and c are integers to be found. [2]

(iv) Rationalise the denominator in $\dfrac{10}{1+\sqrt{2}}$. [2]

3 The derivative of a function is given by $\dfrac{dy}{dx} = \dfrac{1}{2}(x-6)^2 - 16$

(i) Find an expression for y if the graph of y against x is to pass through the point $\left(1, \frac{1}{6}\right)$. [4]

(ii) Evaluate $\displaystyle\int_0^1 y\,dx$. [4]

4 (i) Either algebraically, or by sketching the graphs, solve the inequality $4x + 7 > 7x + 4$ [2]

(ii) Find the values of k, such that $(x-5)(x-3) > k$ for all possible values of x. [3]

(iii) Find the range of x that satisfies the inequality $(x+3)(x-2) < 2$. [4]

5 (i) Sketch the curve $y = (x-2)(x-4)$ and the line $y = 2x - 4$, clearly marking the coordinates of the points of intersection. [3]

(ii) Evaluate the integral $\displaystyle\int_2^4 (x-2)(x-4)\,dx$. [3]

(iii) Hence or otherwise show the total area enclosed by the lines $y = (x-2)(x-4)$ and $y = 2x - 4$ is $\dfrac{32}{3}$. [4]

6 A stall at a fete has a competition where someone draws one card from a pack (minus jokers) and wins points depending on the suit of the card drawn. A person gets one point for a heart, two for a club, three for a diamond and four points for a spade. There are 52 cards in the pack.

a) (i) State the probability of scoring three points. [1]

(ii) Write down the probability of drawing a 7 from the pack, and hence calculate the probability of drawing *either* a 7 *or* a heart. [2]

(iii) Calculate the expected score and the expected variance of the scores. [3]

To make the competition seem more attractive, the scoring system is changed so that a competitor receives 10 points for a heart, 15 for a club, 20 for a diamond and 25 for a spade.

b) (i) Find a relationship of the form $Y = a + bX$ where X and Y are the scores under the old and new systems respectively for the same cards, and hence calculate the new expected score and expected variance. [2]

(ii) If the new scoring system is used, and the prize is one penny for each point scored, what is the minimum amount the organisers should charge in order to expect to make a profit? [1]

7 (i) Find the coordinates of the point A, when A lies at the intersection of the lines l_1 and l_2, and when the equations of l_1 and l_2 respectively are $x - y + 1 = 0$ and $2x + y - 8 = 0$. [3]

(ii) The points B and C have coordinates $(6, -4)$ and $\left(-\frac{4}{3}, -\frac{1}{3}\right)$ respectively, and D is the mid-point of AC. Find the equation of the line BD in the form $ax + by + c = 0$, where a, b and c are integers. [3]

(iii) Show that the triangle ABD is a right-angled triangle, and say which of the sides is parallel to the line $x - y + 4 = 0$. [3]

Paper 1 Q1 — Quadratic Equations

1 (i) Factorise the quadratic expression $x^2 - 2x - 63$. [2]

(ii) Hence find all the solutions to the equation $f(x) = 0$,

where $f(x)$ is given by $f(x) = x^4 - 2x^2 - 63$. [2]

(iii) Find the coordinates of all the stationary points of the graph $y = f(x)$,

and find the gradient at the point $x = 2$. [3]

i | Factorising a quadratic... it must be Christmas

'Factorise the quadratic expression $x^2 - 2x - 63$'

The question tells you to use _factorisation_ — so you know the numbers will be nice and easy.

$$x^2 - 2x - 63 = (x \quad)(x \quad)$$
$$= (x \quad 9)(x \quad 7)$$
$$= (x - 9)(x + 7)$$

So you're solving: $(x - 9)(x + 7) = 0$

and the roots are: $x = 9$ and $x = -7$

For a reminder about how to factorise a quadratic — see pages 5-6.

ii | A Quadratic in Disguise...

'Hence find all the solutions to the equation $f(x) = 0$, where $f(x)$ is given by $f(x) = x^4 - 2x^2 - 63$.'

The question uses the word 'hence' — so you're obviously going to have to use your answer to the part (i) to do this bit...

$f(x) = x^4 - 2x^2 - 63$ ...the new equation looks suspiciously like... $f(x) = x^2 - 2x - 63$

$f(x) = (x^2)^2 - 2(x^2) - 63$ ⟵ *It's just got x²'s instead of x's.*

So if you substitute $y = x^2$ in the new equation $f(y) = y^2 - 2y - 63$

From part (i), this has solutions $y = 9$ **and** $y = -7$

But since –7 is negative, the only possible solutions come from: $x^2 = 9$

which means... $x^2 = 9$ **or** $x^2 = -7$

i.e. $x = \pm 3$

Questions like this are covered on page 13.

iii | A spot of differentiation... mmm, lovely Calculus...

'Find the coordinates of all the stationary points of the graph $y = f(x)$, and find the gradient at the point $x = 2$.'

Stationary points are easy — they're where the derivative (the gradient) has a value of zero. So...

If $\frac{dy}{dx} = 4x^3 - 4x$, put this equal to nought, and factorise

This particular question's actually quite easy — $\frac{dy}{dx} = 0$ when $x = x^3$ so the solution should be obvious.

to get $0 = 4x(x^2 - 1)$
$$= 4x(x - 1)(x + 1)$$
$$\Rightarrow \text{when } \frac{dy}{dx} = 0, \ x = 0, \pm 1$$

Then you get the corresponding y-values by whacking these values of x into the original equation, $y = x^4 - 2x^2 - 63$.

So the stationary points are at (0, –63), (1, –64) and (–1, –64)

Now find the gradient at $x = 2$. Just put $x = 2$ into the expression for the derivative, and hey presto...

$$\frac{dy}{dx} = 4x^3 - 4x = 4 \times 2^3 - 4 \times 2$$
$$= 32 - 8 = 24 \quad \textit{And that's your answer. Smashing.}$$

Calculating quadratics — they're nasty pieces of work...

Two VERY important bits of the course here. QUADRATICS and CALCULUS. Enter exams without them at your peril.

Practice Exam One

Paper 1 Q2 — Powers and Surds

> **2** **(i)** Write down the exact value of $36^{-\frac{1}{2}}$ [2]
>
> **(ii)** Simplify $\dfrac{a^6 \times a^3}{\sqrt{a^4}} \div a^{\frac{1}{2}}$ [2]
>
> **(iii)** Express $\left(5\sqrt{5} + 2\sqrt{3}\right)^2$ in the form $a + b\sqrt{c}$, where a, b and c are integers to be found. [2]
>
> **(iv)** Rationalise the denominator of $\dfrac{10}{\sqrt{5}+1}$. [2]

i | Power Law questions can usually be answered by Rearranging

'Write down the exact value of $36^{-\frac{1}{2}}$.'

With _Power Law_ questions, you usually just have to remember a couple of basic _formulas_, then do a couple of sums pretty darn _carefully_. If you've forgotten any of the Laws, they're all on page 4. So, on with the question...

First get rid of the minus in the exponent / power...

$$x^{-n} = \frac{1}{x^n} \longrightarrow 36^{-\frac{1}{2}} = \frac{1}{36^{\frac{1}{2}}}$$

Then deal with the $\frac{1}{2}$.

$$\frac{1}{36^{\frac{1}{2}}} = \frac{1}{\sqrt{36}} \longleftarrow x^{\frac{1}{n}} = \sqrt[n]{x}$$

And finally...

Do a simple square root. $\longrightarrow \dfrac{1}{\sqrt{36}} = \dfrac{1}{6}$

CHECK YOUR ANSWER:

You can check your answer using your calculator. Just enter:

36 x^y 0.5 $\pm$ =

You should get something like this... $\longrightarrow$ 0.1666667

...and that's roughly a sixth. $\longrightarrow \dfrac{1}{6}$

ii | Simplifying just means Rearranging as well

'Simplify $\dfrac{a^6 \times a^3}{\sqrt{a^4}} \div a^{\frac{1}{2}}$.'

When you're simplifying powers, it's a good idea to get them all looking _the same_. In this example, get the individual bits in the form a^n.

See page 1 for more info on the Power Laws.

First simplify the tricky bit on the bottom of the fraction...

$$\sqrt[m]{a^n} = a^{\frac{n}{m}} \longrightarrow \frac{a^6 \times a^3}{\sqrt{a^4}} \div a^{\frac{1}{2}} = \frac{a^6 \times a^3}{a^2} \div a^{\frac{1}{2}}$$

Then rewrite this so that you're only multiplying things.

$$a^6 \times a^3 \times a^{-2} \times a^{-\frac{1}{2}} \longleftarrow \frac{1}{a^n} = a^{-n}$$

Dividing by a^n is the same as multiplying by a^{-n}.

And then just add all the powers together, to get

$$a^6 \times a^3 \times a^{-2} \times a^{-\frac{1}{2}} = a^{6+3-2-\frac{1}{2}}$$

$$= a^{\frac{13}{2}}$$ Hurray...

CHECK YOUR ANSWER:

$$\frac{a^6 \times a^3}{\sqrt{a^4}} \div a^{\frac{1}{2}} = a^{6\frac{1}{2}}$$ Check your answer by substituting a value for a.

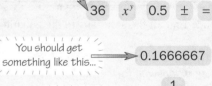

$$\frac{2^6 \times 2^3}{\sqrt{2^4}} \div 2^{\frac{1}{2}} = 2^{6\frac{1}{2}}$$ Work each power of two out separately.

$$\frac{64 \times 8}{4} \div 1.41421 = 90.509$$

Keep lots of decimal places.

$$90.509 = 90.509$$

If both sides are equal, you've got the right answer.

This may sound stupid, but questions on Power Laws aren't too bad, as long as you obey the Power Laws. It really is that simple.

Paper 1 Q2 — Powers and Surds

iii | Multiply out the brackets — then use the rules for _Surds_

'Express $\left(5\sqrt{5}+2\sqrt{3}\right)^2$ in the form $a+b\sqrt{c}$, where a, b and c are integers to be found.'

Yet again, you've got to simplify and rearrange the equation.

First of all (after the initial shock of "Arrrgghh — surds") you should get rid of the <u>squared sign</u> around the brackets.

Multiply out the brackets first:

Multiply this out like a normal quadratic.

$$\left(5\sqrt{5}+2\sqrt{3}\right)^2 = \left(5\sqrt{5}+2\sqrt{3}\right)\times\left(5\sqrt{5}+2\sqrt{3}\right)$$

$$= \left(5\sqrt{5}\right)^2 + 2\left(5\sqrt{5}\times2\sqrt{3}\right) + \left(2\sqrt{3}\right)^2$$

This next bit's a tad confusing, I reckon. You've got three terms to deal with, and they're all a little bit nasty.

The first term is:

$$\left(5\sqrt{5}\right)^2 = 5\sqrt{5}\times5\sqrt{5}$$
$$= 5\times5\times\sqrt{5}\times\sqrt{5}$$
$$= 5\times5\times5$$
$$= 125$$

This is a times sign, not an add sign — so don't 'work out' the brackets.

The second term is:

$$2\left(5\sqrt{5}\times2\sqrt{3}\right) = 2\times5\times2\times\sqrt{5}\times\sqrt{3}$$
$$= 20\times\sqrt{15}$$
$$= 20\sqrt{15}$$

Remember — the <u>order</u> doesn't matter when you multiply.

$\sqrt{5}\sqrt{3} = \sqrt{5\times3} = \sqrt{15}$. _Whatever you do, <u>don't</u> add the numbers in the square root signs._

And the third term is:

$$\left(2\sqrt{3}\right)^2 = 2\sqrt{3}\times2\sqrt{3}$$
$$= 2\times2\times\sqrt{3}\times\sqrt{3}$$
$$= 2\times2\times3$$
$$= 12$$

$\sqrt{3}\times\sqrt{3} = 3$

Now you've done that, though, you're almost home and dry. All that's left to do is add the three terms together.

So the whole thing's equal to...

$$125 + 20\sqrt{15} + 12 = 137 + 20\sqrt{15}$$

And since 137, 20 and 15 are all <u>integers</u>, this is the final answer to the question.

iv | Rationalise by multiplying top and bottom lines by the _Same Thing_

'Rationalise the denominator of $\frac{10}{\sqrt{5}+1}$.'

Rationalising a denominator means getting rid of surds on the bottom line of a fraction. Sounds hard — but it's easy.

The first thing to do is rewrite the bottom line so that it's in the form $a+\sqrt{b}$ — with the surd <u>after</u> the + or – sign.

If the bottom line doesn't already have the surd <u>after</u> the + or –...

$$\frac{10}{\sqrt{5}+1} = \frac{10}{1+\sqrt{5}}$$

...just rewrite the bottom line.

Then if you've got $a+\sqrt{b}$ on the bottom line — you have to multiply <u>top</u> and <u>bottom</u> lines by $a-\sqrt{b}$, and vice versa.

$$\frac{10}{1+\sqrt{5}} = \frac{10}{1+\sqrt{5}} \times \frac{1-\sqrt{5}}{1-\sqrt{5}}$$
$$= \frac{10(1-\sqrt{5})}{(1+\sqrt{5})(1-\sqrt{5})}$$
$$= \frac{10(1-\sqrt{5})}{1-5}$$
$$= \frac{10(1-\sqrt{5})}{-4} = \frac{-5(1-\sqrt{5})}{2}$$

Since the bottom line is $1+\sqrt{5}$, you have to multiply both the top and bottom lines by $1-\sqrt{5}$.

Use the difference of two squares:
$$(x + y)(x - y) = x^2 - y^2.$$

Just change the sign before the surd — and multiply top and bottom lines by it.

Keep your Magic Power Laws close to you at all times...

I don't want to go on and on and start ranting but... hang on a bit, I <u>do</u> want to go on and on, and I <u>do</u> want to rant. The thing is that questions on the Power Laws <u>always</u> come up in the exams and are <u>always</u> worth a <u>good few marks</u>. And those few marks could make the difference between one grade and the next. Think about it — half an hour spent learning this page really well could move you up a grade. You know it makes sense...

Paper 1 Q3 — Calculus

3   The derivative of a function is given by $\frac{dy}{dx} = \frac{1}{2}(x-6)^2 - 16$

   (i)   Find an expression for y if the graph of y against x is to pass through the point $\left(1, \frac{1}{6}\right)$.   [4]

   (ii)   Evaluate $\int_0^1 y\,dx$.   [4]

i   You just Integrate it...

'Find an expression for y if the graph of y against x is to pass through the point $\left(1, \frac{1}{6}\right)$.'

To get an expression for y from an expression for $\frac{dy}{dx}$, you just _integrate_.

(Integration is the opposite of differentiation, remember.)

Before you can integrate it, you have to rewrite $\frac{dy}{dx}$ as 'de-simplified' _powers of x_...

$$\frac{dy}{dx} = \frac{1}{2}(x-6)^2 - 16$$
$$= \frac{1}{2}\{x^2 - 12x + 36\} - 16$$
$$= \frac{1}{2}x^2 - 6x + 2$$

Expand the brackets to get separate coefficients for separate powers of x.

Now write both sides as integrals...

Just put an integral sign and 'dx' around both sides for now. $\longrightarrow$ $\int \frac{dy}{dx}dx = \int\left(\frac{1}{2}x^2 - 6x + 2\right)dx$

Integrate the left-hand side and you get y. Integrate the right-hand side, and you get...

$$y = \frac{x^3}{6} - 3x^2 + 2x + C$$

Integrating $\frac{dy}{dx}$ gives y.

Don't forget that constant of integration.

If you wanted to practise, or you had a really difficult expression to integrate, don't forget — you could have split up the integral into 3 separate bits:

The integration formula:

$$\int x^n dx = \frac{x^{n+1}}{n+1} + C$$

Integrate each term separately...

$$y = \frac{1}{2}\int x^2 dx - 6\int x\,dx + \int 2\,dx$$

Don't forget the signs (+'s and –'s). I'm just showing the actual integrals — not their mathematical persuasion!

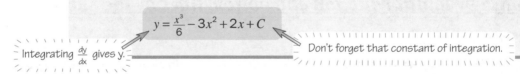

$$\frac{1}{2}\left(\frac{x^3}{3}\right) \quad 6\left(\frac{x^2}{2}\right) \quad 2x$$

Get the signs right. $\longrightarrow$ $y = \frac{x^3}{6} - 3x^2 + 2x + C$ ...and add a _constant of integration_.

You always have to stick in a constant of integration — you don't know what it is yet, so call it C for now.

You might wonder why there's only one constant. Since you've had to do four separate mini-integrations, shouldn't there be four constants like this?

$$y + C_1 = \frac{x^3}{6} + C_2 - 3x^2 + C_3 + 2x + C_4$$

Well yes, but rather than have four separate ones, you can just make them into one.

Let $C = -C_1 + C_2 + C_3 + C_4 \Rightarrow y = \frac{x^3}{6} - 3x^2 + 2x + C$

Paper 1 Q3 — Calculus

...and then stick in the Values it gives for x and y

'...to pass through the point $\left(1, \frac{1}{6}\right)$.'

To make sure the curve goes through the right point, you have to find the correct value for C.

To do this, stick in the values $x = 1$ and $y = \frac{1}{6}$, and the value of C will just pop out.

Substitute $x = 1$ and $y = \frac{1}{6}$ in the expression for y...

$$y = \frac{x^3}{6} - 3x^2 + 2x + C$$
$$\Rightarrow \frac{1}{6} = \frac{1^3}{6} - \left(3 \times 1^2\right) + \left(2 \times 1\right) + C$$
$$\Rightarrow \frac{1}{6} = \frac{1}{6} - 1 + C$$
$$\Rightarrow C = 1$$

And so the complete expression for y is...

$$y = \frac{x^3}{6} - 3x^2 + 2x + 1$$

You should check your answer by:

(i) putting in $x = 1$ (and making sure you get $\frac{1}{6}$)

and (ii) differentiating it (and making sure you get the derivative in the question).

ii | A simple Limit Integral — but don't fall into the Trap

'Evaluate $\int_0^1 y\,dx$.'

This part is pretty standard stuff — but there's a really obvious trap at the start. As long as you avoid that, you can't go far wrong.

You need to find $\int_0^1 y\,dx$.

Now the 'dx' means you're integrating with respect to x. So you need to write y in terms of x before you integrate. But that's what you've just found — so stick in your answer to part (i).

THE TRAP:

$$\int_0^1 y\,dx = \left[\frac{y^2}{2}\right]_0^1 = \frac{1}{2} - 0 = \frac{1}{2}$$

This answer's rubbish! It's integrating with respect to y, when it should be x.

$$\int_0^1 y\,dx = \int_0^1 \left(\frac{x^3}{6} - 3x^2 + 2x + 1\right)dx$$

You could break this up into individual chunks like before — but you don't have to. Do whatever's easier.

It's a limit integral, so integrate the bracket — and stick it in a big square bracket with limits.

$$\int_0^1 y\,dx = \int_0^1 \left(\frac{x^3}{6} - 3x^2 + 2x + 1\right)dx = \left[\frac{x^4}{6 \times 4} - \frac{3x^3}{3} + \frac{2x^2}{2} + \frac{1x^1}{1}\right]_0^1$$
$$= \left[\frac{x^4}{24} - x^3 + x^2 + x\right]_0^1$$

Now evaluate the square bracket — use the top limit first, then subtract what you get when you use the bottom limit.

$$\int_0^1 y\,dx = \left(\frac{1^4}{24} - 1^3 + 1^2 + 1\right) - \left(\frac{0^4}{24} - 0^3 + 0^2 + 0\right)$$
$$= \frac{1}{24} - 1 + 1 + 1$$
$$= \frac{25}{24}$$

When you put $x = 0$, all these parts are equal to zero.

Integration — I'n't it great? ...no? Oh... didn't think so...

This question is a gift — it's all real standard stuff. So if you're struggling with it, bury your head in those maths books until it begins to make sense. And another thing — always make sure you use all the info the question gives you, e.g. if it says the graph passes through the point (joe, bloggs), it means "at some point in the question, you need to plug in the values x=joe when y=bloggs". And watch for that trap at the end — the 'dx' in an integral means you have to integrate x's.

Paper 1 Q4 — Inequalities

> **4 (i)** Either algebraically, or by sketching the graphs, solve the inequality
> $$4x + 7 > 7x + 4$$
> [2]
> **(ii)** Find the values of k, such that
> $$(x-5)(x-3) > k \text{ for all possible values of } x.$$
> [3]
> **(iii)** Find the range of x that satisfies the inequality
> $$(x+3)(x-2) < 2.$$
> [4]

i | A straightforward Linear Inequality

'Either algebraically, or by sketching the graphs...'

*That opening makes it sound really tricky, but don't be fooled. Sketching graphs sounds much easier, but it's such a **simple** inequality that it's much quicker to just work it out:*

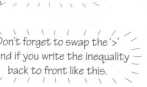

$$4x + 7 > 7x + 4$$
$$3 > 3x$$
$$x < 1$$

Subtracting 4x and 4 from both sides.

Don't forget to swap the '>' round if you write the inequality back to front like this.

4x + 7 > 7x + 4 if x < 1

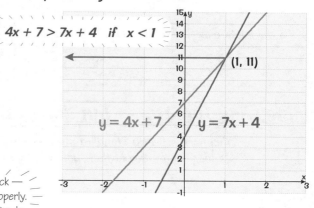

(1, 11)

$y = 4x + 7$ $y = 7x + 4$

There — that wasn't so bad.

Of course, it doesn't hurt to sketch the graphs just to check — and it's a good idea to make sure you can interpret them properly. But to be honest, they don't make the question any easier to do.

ii | Easy — if you spot the Symmetry

'Find the values of k such that
$$(x-5)(x-3) > k \text{ for all possible values of } x.'$$

Basically, you've got to find the *minimum* value of $(x-5)(x-3)$, and make sure k is less than that.

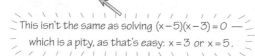

This isn't the same as solving $(x-5)(x-3) = 0$ — which is a pity, as that's easy: x = 3 or x = 5.

> You could do this by <u>Completing the Square</u> as well. You need to find k, with:
> $$k < (x-5)(x-3) \Rightarrow k < x^2 - 8x + 15$$
> $$\Rightarrow k < (x-4)^2 - 1$$
> So as long as k < −1, this'll be true.

As always, if you're a bit unsure where to start, think what the function looks like — and *SKETCH THE GRAPH*.

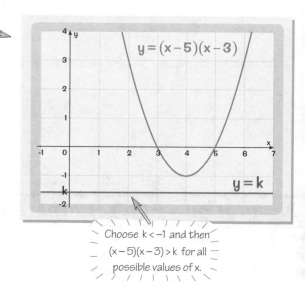

$y = (x-5)(x-3)$

$y = k$

Here's the cunning bit: The thing to realise is that the graph's *symmetrical* — so the minimum will be halfway between x = 3 and x = 5 — i.e. x = 4. So just plug that into the equation to find the lowest point the graph reaches:

Putting x = 4 in (x − 5)(x − 3) gives
$$(4-5)(4-3) = -1 \times 1$$
$$= -1$$
So if k < −1, the graph will never be as low as k.

Choose k < −1 and then $(x-5)(x-3) > k$ for all possible values of x.

Paper 1 Q4 — Inequalities

iii | Draw the Graph to see when it's Negative

'Find the range of x that satisfies the inequality

$$(x+3)(x-2) < 2 \text{.'}$$

You need to find a 'range of x' — not just one value. Sounds a bit complicated — but it's not too bad once you get going. The first thing to do is rearrange the equation so you've got <u>zero</u> on one side.

Rearrange the expression to get...

$$(x+3)(x-2) < 2$$
$$x^2 + x - 6 < 2$$
$$x^2 + x - 8 < 0$$

Rearrange this to get zero on one side. Then when you draw the graph, all you need to do is find where the graph is negative.

Then sketch the graph of $y = x^2 + x - 8$. And since you're interested in when this is less than zero, make sure you find out where this crosses the <u>x-axis</u>.

When the graph crosses the x-axis, it changes from positive to negative, or vice versa.

Now $x^2 + x - 8$ doesn't factorise — so find out where it crosses the x-axis by using the <u>quadratic formula</u>.

You can tell it doesn't factorise because $\sqrt{b^2 - 4ac} = \sqrt{33} = 5.74456...$ — and that's not a whole number or an 'easy' decimal.

Now, $x^2 + x - 8 = 0$ when

$$x = \frac{-1 \pm \sqrt{1^2 - (4 \times 1 \times -8)}}{2 \times 1}$$
$$= \frac{-1 \pm \sqrt{33}}{2}$$

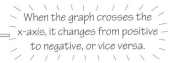

The quadratic formula:
If $ax^2 + bx + c = 0$,
then
$$x = \frac{-b \pm \sqrt{b^2 - 4ac}}{2a}$$

So the graph looks like this:

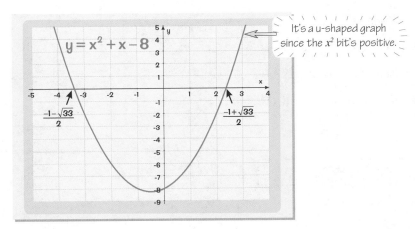

$$y = x^2 + x - 8$$

It's a u-shaped graph since the x^2 bit's positive.

And since you need this to be <u>negative</u> — it's pretty clear that the range of x you're interested in is...

$$\frac{-1 - \sqrt{33}}{2} < x < \frac{-1 + \sqrt{33}}{2}$$

$a < x < b$ means 'x between a and b'.

or... $-3.37 < x < 2.37$ *(to 2 d.p.)*

It's easy to check — just stick the two numbers back into the original inequality and make sure the left-hand side equals 2.

These can be pretty darn hard unless you draw the graphs...

It's true. These questions can be very hard unless you have a picture to look at. It just helps you understand exactly what's going on, and what the examiners are going on about. That's the thing with these questions — they can look so intimidating. But drawing a picture helps you get your head round it — and once you've got your head round it, it's much easier to work towards the answer. Mmmm... I think I've said enough on that for now.

Paper 1 Q5 — Simultaneous Equations

5 **(i)** Sketch the curve $y = (x-2)(x-4)$ and the line $y = 2x-4$ on the same set of axes, clearly
marking the coordinates of the points of intersection. [3]

(ii) Evaluate the integral $\int_2^4 (x-2)(x-4)\,dx$. [3]

(iii) Hence or otherwise show the total area enclosed by the lines $y = (x-2)(x-4)$ and $y = 2x-4$ is $\frac{32}{3}$. [4]

i | Solve some Simultaneous Equations and Sketch a Curve

'Sketch the curve $y = (x-2)(x-4)$ and the line $y = 2x-4$ ...'

*The question says you have to mark in the coordinates of the points where the parabola and the straight line cross.
It's probably a good idea to find these before you draw anything — and that means solving simultaneous equations.*

So solve these simultaneous equations to find the intersection points.

$$y = (x-2)(x-4) \quad \text{①}$$
$$y = 2x-4 \quad \text{②}$$

It's best to label them first.

Simultaneous equations where one of them is quadratic — straight away, think substitution. So...

Ⓐ Substitute y from equation 2 into equation 1:

$$2x-4 = (x-2)(x-4)$$
$$\Rightarrow 2x-4 = x^2 - 6x + 8$$

Rearrange things so that everything is on one side and you get...

$$x^2 - 8x + 12 = 0$$
$$\Rightarrow (x-2)(x-6) = 0$$
$$\Rightarrow x = 2 \quad or \quad x = 6$$

These are the x-coordinates of the points of intersection.

Now find the y-coordinates:

$$x = 2 \quad \text{in equation 2} \Rightarrow y = (2 \times 2) - 4 = 0$$

$$x = 6 \quad \text{in equation 2} \Rightarrow y = (2 \times 6) - 4 = 8$$

So the two points of intersection are: **(2, 0) and (6, 8)**.

Ⓑ *Then drawing the graph is easy. The parabola
crosses the x-axis at x = 2 and x = 4, and it
crosses the line at x = 2 and x = 6.*

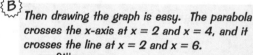

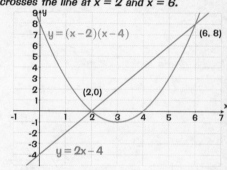

*It's a u-shaped parabola, since
the coefficient of x² is positive.*   *The line has
gradient 2.*

ii | A pretty easy Integration

'Evaluate the integral $\int_2^4 (x-2)(x-4)\,dx$.'

A pretty standard integration — shouldn't cause too many problems really...

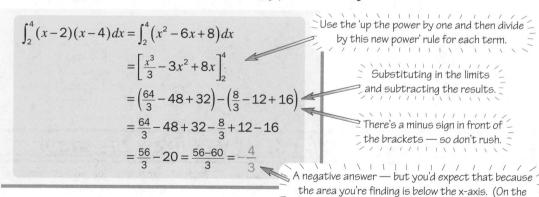

$$\int_2^4 (x-2)(x-4)\,dx = \int_2^4 (x^2 - 6x + 8)\,dx$$

*Use the 'up the power by one and then divide
by this new power' rule for each term.*

$$= \left[\frac{x^3}{3} - 3x^2 + 8x \right]_2^4$$

*Substituting in the limits
and subtracting the results.*

$$= \left(\frac{64}{3} - 48 + 32 \right) - \left(\frac{8}{3} - 12 + 16 \right)$$

*There's a minus sign in front of
the brackets — so don't rush.*

$$= \frac{64}{3} - 48 + 32 - \frac{8}{3} + 12 - 16$$

$$= \frac{56}{3} - 20 = \frac{56-60}{3} = -\frac{4}{3}$$

*A negative answer — but you'd expect that because
the area you're finding is below the x-axis. (On the
graph, it's the area where the parabola's negative.)*

Paper 1 Q5 — Simultaneous Equations

iii | Finding the Area between Two lines — use your Sketch

'Hence or otherwise show the total area enclosed by the lines $y = (x-2)(x-4)$ and $y = 2x-4$ is $\frac{32}{3}$.'

This looks a bit tricky. Have another look at the graph to work out exactly what you've got to do.

You need the total area between the lines.
This is: the green area B + the yellow area A.

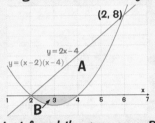

You've just found the green area B.
Now you need to work out the yellow area A.

The yellow area is:

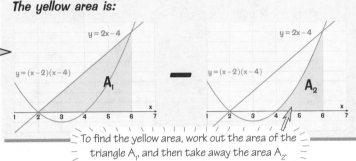

To find the yellow area, work out the area of the triangle A_1, and then take away the area A_2.

① The area of the triangle A_1 is given by:

$$A_1 = \frac{1}{2} \times base \times height$$
$$= \frac{1}{2} \times 4 \times 8 = 16$$

② The area you need to subtract, A_2, is:

$$A_2 = \int_4^6 (x-2)(x-4)\,dx = \int_4^6 \left(x^2 - 6x + 8\right)dx$$
$$= \left[\frac{x^3}{3} - 3x^2 + 8x\right]_4^6$$
$$= \left(\frac{216}{3} - 108 + 48\right) - \left(\frac{64}{3} - 48 + 32\right)$$
$$= \frac{152}{3} - 44 = \frac{152 - 132}{3} = \frac{20}{3}$$

③ So the yellow area A is: $A = A_1 - A_2$

$$= 16 - \frac{20}{3} = \frac{48 - 20}{3} = \frac{28}{3}$$

④ And the total area enclosed by the two lines is:

$$Total\ area = yellow\ area + green\ area$$
$$= \frac{28}{3} + \frac{4}{3} = \frac{32}{3}$$

> The integral you found in part (ii) had a minus sign — but you have to ignore it here. The minus sign tells you that the area is below the x-axis, but that's not important here — you just need to know the actual area.

But there's another way to find the Area between two lines...

There is a quicker way to do this — but it's not as easy to see why it works.

If you 'subtract' the lower line from the one that's higher up, and then integrate what you get — you find the area between them.

$$Area\ between\ the\ lines = \int_2^6 \{(top\ line) - (bottom\ line)\}dx$$
$$= \int_2^6 \{(2x-4) - (x^2 - 6x + 8)\}dx$$
$$= \int_2^6 (-x^2 + 8x - 12)dx$$
$$= \left[-\frac{x^3}{3} + 4x^2 - 12x\right]_2^6$$
$$= \left(-\frac{216}{3} + 144 - 72\right) - \left(-\frac{8}{3} + 16 - 24\right)$$
$$= -\frac{208}{3} + 80 = \frac{-208 + 240}{3} = \frac{32}{3}$$

Between x = 2 and x = 6, the line is higher than the parabola, so take the equation of the parabola from the equation of the straight line.

A-Level Maths: You shouldn't have done it if you can't take a joke...

There's nothing massively hard in this question, but there are bits that might catch you out if you're not paying attention, like that stuff about ignoring the minus sign (which is pretty confusing, I admit). The bit at the end about 'subtracting the lines' is just a quick way to do the same stuff that's on the top half of the page (i.e. finding the area between two lines). If you don't get it, it doesn't matter — the top way's easier anyway. But it might save a bit of time...

Practice Exam One

Paper 1 Q6 — Probability...

6 A stall at a fete has a competition where someone draws one card from a pack (minus jokers) and wins points depending on the suit of the card drawn. A person gets one point for a heart, two for a club, three for a diamond and four points for a spade. There are 52 cards in the pack.

   a) (i)   State the probability of scoring three points. [1]

      (ii) Write down the probability of drawing a 7 from the pack, and hence calculate the probability of drawing *either* a 7 *or* a heart. [2]

      (iii) Calculate the expected score and the expected variance of the scores. [3]

   To make the competition seem more attractive, the scoring system is changed so that a competitor receives 10 points for a heart, 15 for a club, 20 for a diamond and 25 for a spade.

   b) (i)   Find a relationship of the form $Y = a + bX$ where X and Y are the scores under the old and new systems respectively for the same cards, and hence calculate the new expected score and expected variance. [2]

      (ii) If the new scoring system is used, and the prize is one penny for each point scored, what is the minimum amount the organisers should charge in order to expect to make a profit? [1]

(a) i | This one really is a Gift...

'State the probability of scoring three points.'

The answer is obvious — there are four suits, each with 13 cards, so the answer is a quarter — you can only score three with a diamond. If you wanted to look good in the exam though, you'd write down something like this:

> *There are 52 cards. There are 13 diamonds. A separate score is assigned to each suit.*
>
> *So, if P(D) is the probability of scoring three points (or getting a diamond), then...*
>
> $$P(D) = \frac{n(D)}{n(S)} = \frac{13}{52} = \frac{1}{4}$$

This uses the notation on p42:
P(D) = probability of getting a diamond
n(D) = number of cards in the suit
n(S) = number of cards in the pack
Here D is the event, and S is the whole thing.

(a) ii | Use those wonderful and/or Formulas...

'Write down the probability of drawing a 7 from the pack, and hence calculate the probability of drawing *either* a 7 *or* a heart.'

There are 4 suits, so there are 4 sevens. Use this, then the formula for P(A or B) to find your answer...

First designate letters to the separate probabilities:

Probability of getting a heart: $P(H)$ *Probability of getting a seven:* $P(7)$

Work out the separate probabilities. Plug them in the formula...

$P(7) = \frac{4}{52} = \frac{1}{13}$

$P(H) = \frac{13}{52} = \frac{1}{4}$

$P(7 \cap H) = P(7 \text{ of hearts}) = \frac{1}{52}$

$P(7 \cup H) = P(7) + P(H) - P(7 \cap H)$

$\qquad = \frac{1}{13} + \frac{1}{4} - \frac{1}{52}$

$\qquad = \frac{4}{13}$

Here's a little reminder of some lovely formulas you'll almost certainly need...
$P(A \cup B) = P(A \text{ or } B)$
$\qquad\qquad = P(A) + P(B) - P(A \cap B)$
$P(A \cap B) = P(A \text{ and } B)$
$Var(aX + b) = a^2 Var(X)$

(a) iii | Well, what did you Expect...

'Calculate the expected score and the expected variance of the scores.'

Aaaah, that lovely word. And d'you know what? You probably wouldn't even notice it if you weren't looking for it. Expected. Ooh, it sends shivers down my spine. No, really — it does. It scares the living daylights out of me. This horrible little word means you've got to remember to use those darned complicated formulas...

Paper 1 Q6 — ...and Statistics

...So you also need different notation...☺

If **X** is the score... $x_1 = 1$ $x_3 = 3$ $x_2 = 2$ $x_4 = 4$ ...which means:

$$p_1 = P(X = x_1) = \frac{13}{52} = \frac{1}{4}$$

$$p_3 = P(X = x_3) = \frac{13}{52} = \frac{1}{4}$$

$$p_2 = P(X = x_2) = \frac{13}{52} = \frac{1}{4}$$

$$p_4 = P(X = x_4) = \frac{13}{52} = \frac{1}{4}$$

The expected score is written as **E(X)**. The expected variance is **Var(X)**. Don't forget their lovely little formulas...

You need this...   This value is sometimes known as μ.

$$E(X) = \sum_i x_i p_i$$

$$= \left(1 \cdot \frac{1}{4}\right) + \left(2 \cdot \frac{1}{4}\right) + \left(3 \cdot \frac{1}{4}\right) + \left(4 \cdot \frac{1}{4}\right)$$

$$= \frac{10}{4} = \frac{5}{2}$$

...and this...

$$E(X^2) = \sum_i x_i^2 p_i$$

$$= \left(1 \cdot \frac{1}{4}\right) + \left(4 \cdot \frac{1}{4}\right) + \left(9 \cdot \frac{1}{4}\right) + \left(16 \cdot \frac{1}{4}\right)$$

$$= \frac{30}{4} = \frac{15}{2}$$

...to find this.

$$Var(X) = E(X^2) - [E(X)]^2$$

$$= \frac{15}{2} - \left[\frac{5}{2}\right]^2$$

$$= \frac{5}{4}$$

Make your final answer CLEAR. ⟹ **So, the expected score is** $\frac{5}{2}$. **And the expected variance is** $\frac{5}{4}$.

(b) i | *Convert the old variance*

'Find a relationship of the form $Y = a + bX$ where X and Y are the scores under the old and new systems respectively for the same cards, and hence calculate the new expected score and expected variance.'

Work out what's become what. Compare them, then work out what numbers to pop in the conversion formula. They've already told you what relationship to look out for in the question. Easy really...

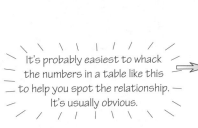

It's probably easiest to whack the numbers in a table like this to help you spot the relationship. It's usually obvious.

X	Y
1	→ 10
2	→ 15
3	→ 20
4	→ 25

These values tell you that $Y = 5 + 5X$ ⟸ Use the form they give you in the question.

And so

$$E(Y) = 5 + 5E(X)$$

$$= 5 + \left(5 \cdot \frac{5}{2}\right)$$

$$= \frac{35}{2}$$

And

$$Var(Y) = Var(5 + 5X)$$

$$= 5^2 \times Var(X)$$

$$= 25 \times \frac{5}{4}$$

$$= \frac{125}{4}$$

(b) ii | *Using statistics for Profit...*

'If the new scoring system is used, and the prize is one penny for each point scored, what is the minimum amount the organisers should charge in order to expect to make a profit?'

Sit back and enjoy the ride — they're just trying to confuse you here. You've already worked out everything you need to answer this question. The number of pence won is exactly the same as the number of points won before, so just look at the values you got before...

You're using the new scoring system so you want to know the expected value of Y:

$$E(Y) = 5 + 5E(X)$$

You know this from before. ⟹

$$= 5 + \left(5 \cdot \frac{5}{2}\right)$$

$$= \frac{35}{2}$$

This is the expected number of points won — so it's the same as the amount of prize money expected to be paid out.

So they need to charge more than 17.5p per go in order to expect to make a profit. You can't charge fractional pennies so... the minimum they can charge is **18p**.

When the question says jump — you ask, 'How high...'

Just like always — read the question and give the examiners what they ask for — coffee, biscuits, a slap-up meal...

Paper 1 Q7 — Geometry

7 **(i)** Find the coordinates of the point A, when A lies at the intersection of the lines l_1 and l_2, and when the equations of l_1 and l_2 respectively are $x - y + 1 = 0$ and $2x + y - 8 = 0$. **[3]**

(ii) The points B and C have coordinates $(6, -4)$ and $\left(-\frac{4}{3}, -\frac{1}{3}\right)$ respectively, and D is the midpoint of AC. Find the equation of the line BD in the form $ax + by + c = 0$, where a, b and c are integers. **[3]**

(iii) Show that the triangle ABD is a right-angled triangle, and say which of the sides is parallel to the line $x - y + 4 = 0$ **[3]**

---

i | **Finding A is easy — it's just** Simultaneous Equations...

'Find the coordinates of the point A...'

A is the point where these two lines intersect. So to find its coordinates, you need to solve the equations of the two lines as a pair of simultaneous equations.

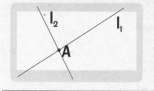

Line 1 — ①⃝ — $x - y + 1 = 0$

Line 2 — ②⃝ — $2x + y - 8 = 0$

Get rid of y to find x:

①⃝ + ②⃝ $(x + 2x) + (-y + y) + (1 - 8) = 0$

$$3x - 7 = 0$$

$$x = \tfrac{7}{3}$$

Stick x=7/3 back into l_1 to find y:

①⃝ $x - y + 1 = 0$

$$\tfrac{7}{3} - y + 1 = 0$$

$$y = \tfrac{7}{3} + 1 = \tfrac{10}{3}$$

So A is $\left(\tfrac{7}{3}, \tfrac{10}{3}\right)$.

Forgotten everything you ever knew about simultaneous equations? Have a look at page 17.

---

ii | **Equation of a line — find the** Gradient First...

'Find the equation of the line BD in the form $ax + by + c = 0$...'

This question gives you loads of information. So draw a sketch. Otherwise you won't have a clue what's going on. (Well I wouldn't anyway.)

To find the equation of a line, you'll need its gradient.

And to find the gradient of BD, you'll need the coordinates of B and D — you're given B in the question, but you've got to find D.

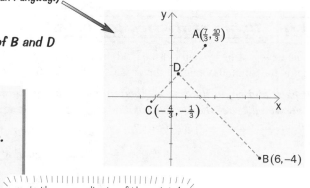

FIND D (THE MIDPOINT OF A AND C)

You get the midpoint of two points by finding the average of the x-coordinates, and the average of the y-coordinates.

Midpoint of AC is... $\left(\dfrac{x_A + x_C}{2}, \dfrac{y_A + y_C}{2}\right)$

x_A is the x-coordinate of the point A.
y_C is the y-coordinate of the point C.

which is... $= \left(\dfrac{\frac{7}{3} + \frac{-4}{3}}{2}, \dfrac{\frac{10}{3} + \frac{-1}{3}}{2}\right) = \left(\tfrac{1}{2}, \tfrac{3}{2}\right)$

So D is... $\left(\tfrac{1}{2}, \tfrac{3}{2}\right)$

FIND THE GRADIENT OF BD

$$\text{Gradient} = \frac{\text{difference in y-coordinates}}{\text{difference in x-coordinates}}$$

m_{BD} is the gradient of the line BD.

$$m_{BD} = \frac{y_D - y_B}{x_D - x_B} = \frac{\frac{3}{2} - (-4)}{\frac{1}{2} - 6} = \frac{\frac{11}{2}}{-\frac{11}{2}} = -1$$

Paper 1 Q7 — Geometry

So you've got the gradient... Well now you can do anything — you can sail around the world, you can become the richest person in the world, you can rule the world... you can become more powerful than you can possibly imagine...

| FIND THE EQUATION OF BD | $y = mx + c$ is probably the easiest form for the equation of a straight line. So...

The equation will be like this because the gradient is –1 — you just need to find c. → $y = m_{BD}x + c \Rightarrow y = -x + c$

Putting in the values for x and y at either point B or point D will give you the value of c.

At point B,
$x = 6$ and $y = -4$

$y = mx + c$
$-4 = -6 + c$
$c = 2$

So equation for BD is: $y = -x + 2$

$x + y - 2 = 0$

Make sure it's in the form the question asks for.

$y = mx + c$ is great — m is the gradient, and c is where the line crosses the y axis.

iii | Right-angled triangle? Check if the lines are Perpendicular

'Show that the triangle ABD is a right-angled triangle,...'

The first thing to do is update your sketch (or do a new one) with the triangle ABD on.

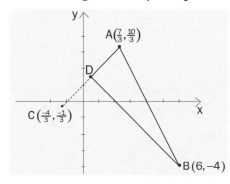

A$(\frac{7}{3}, \frac{10}{3})$
D
C$(\frac{-4}{3}, \frac{-1}{3})$
B$(6, -4)$

You've got to show that ABD is right-angled. To do this, just show that two sides of the triangle are perpendicular to each other (so their gradients multiply to give –1).

(That means you'll have a right angle in the corner where the sides meet.)

See page 24 for more info on perpendicular lines.

Show that the gradients of AD and BD multiply together to give –1:

Gradient of AD: $m_{DA} = \dfrac{y_D - y_A}{x_D - x_A} = \dfrac{\frac{3}{2} - \frac{10}{3}}{\frac{1}{2} - \frac{7}{3}} = \dfrac{9 - 20}{3 - 14} = 1$

And you already know the gradient of BD is: $m_{BD} = -1$

So... $m_{BD} \times m_{DA} = -1 \times 1 = -1$

So angle ADB is a right-angle. Fantastic.

Gradients of perpendicular lines multiply together to make –1.

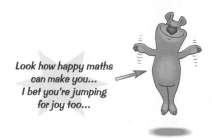

Look how happy maths can make you...
I bet you're jumping for joy too...

'...and say which of the sides is parallel to the line $x - y + 4 = 0$'

Finding the edge parallel to $x - y + 4 = 0$ would be easier if you rearranged this into $y = mx + c$ form. (Like before!)

$x - y + 4 = 0 \Rightarrow y = x + 4$

The gradient of this line is 1, so you need to find which side of the triangle also has a gradient of 1 — this is line AD.

The gradient of AD and the line $x - y + 4 + 0$ both have a gradient of 1, so these two lines must be parallel.

So you've proved it's a right-angled triangle, found the parallel edge and completed a stinker of a question. Now...

...become the Master of the Universe...

To avoid getting into trouble while you're doing this question, you've got to draw what's happening before you do each part. So when you read stuff like "The points B and C have coordinates (6,–4) and..." you should dive for your pencil and sketch all the information it gives you. And then use the sketch and plan how you're going to answer the question.

1 **(i)** Express $x^2 - 7x + 17$ in the form $(x-a)^2 + b$, where a and b are constants.

Hence state the maximum value of $f(x) = \dfrac{1}{x^2 - 7x + 17}$. [2]

(ii) Find the possible values of b if the equation $g(x) = 0$ is to have only one root,

where $g(x)$ is given by $g(x) = 3x^2 + bx + 12$. [3]

2 The function $g(x)$ is defined by $g(x) = (x-5)(x-3)(x+7)$.

(i) Show that the rate of change of $g(x)$ with respect to x can be written $g'(x) = 3x^2 - 2x - 41$. [2]

(ii) Hence find the x-coordinates of the stationary points of $g(x)$ to three decimal places. [3]

(iii) Find, to 3 dp, the ranges of x for which $g(x)$ is: (a) an increasing function of x;

(b) a decreasing function of x. [3]

(iv) If $f(x) = x^3 + 3x^2 + kx + 7$, find the possible values of k so that $f(x)$ has no turning points. [3]

3 A worker in a duck sanctuary measured the weights of the sanctuary's adult ducks. The following data was collected:

Weight in grams	<1000	1000-1200	1200-1400	1400-1500	1500-1600	1600-1800	1800-2000	2000-2500	2500-3000
Frequency	2	5	5	8	13	18	8	3	1

(a) **(i)** Calculate suitable frequency densities and, on graph paper, construct a histogram of the data. [3]

(ii) Calculate estimates of the mean and variance of the weights of the ducks. [3]

(b) **(i)** Represent this information using a cumulative percentage frequency diagram. [3]

(ii) Estimate the median, lower quartile and upper quartile weights of the ducks. [2]

(iii) Use your estimates to draw an approximate box and whisker diagram of the results. [2]

4 **(i)** Rewrite the following expression in the form $f(x) = 0$, where f(x) is of the form $f(x) = ax^3 + bx^2 + cx + d$.

$$(x-1)(x^2 + x + 1) = 2x^2 - 17$$ [2]

(ii) Show that $(x+2)$ is a factor of f(x). [2]

(iii) Using your answer to part (iii), factorise $f(x)$ as the product of a linear factor and a quadratic factor. [3]

(iv) By completing the square, or otherwise, show that $f(x) = 0$ has no other roots. [2]

5 A new symmetrical mini-stage is to be built according to the design shown in the diagram.

(i) Find expressions for x and y in terms of r. [2]

(ii) Find, in terms of r and q, expressions for the perimeter P, and the area A, of the stage. [3]

(iii) If the perimeter of the stage is to be 40 metres, show that

A is given by $A = 20r - \dfrac{r^2}{16}\left(9 + 4\sqrt{2}\right)$. [3]

(iv) By finding $\dfrac{dA}{dr}$ show that the maximum possible area of the stage is $A_{max} = \dfrac{1600}{9 + 4\sqrt{2}}$. [3]

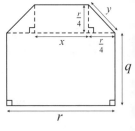

6 In a multiple-choice exam, where each question has five alternative answers, only one being correct, it is estimated that 75% of all students will know the answer to the first question. If a student definitely knows the answer to the question, it has been found that the probability of that student making a mistake and recording the wrong answer is 0.02. If a student doesn't know the answer, he or she will guess the answer, with a one in five chance of success.

(a)(i) If an answer paper is selected at random, what is the probability that the answer to the first question is correct? [2]

(ii) If a random answer paper is checked and is found to have the correct answer to the first question, what is the probability that the student actually knew which answer was correct and didn't have to guess? [2]

(iii) Are the events 'student knows the answer' and 'student gets question correct' independent? Explain your answer mathematically. [2]

For one particular class of fifteen students, the marks in the test were as shown below:

53, 47, 94, 84, 78, 63, 91, 45, 66, 66, 59, 62, 51, 68, 72

(b)(i) Draw an appropriate stem and leaf diagram to illustrate these results. [2]

(ii) State the range of the data, and calculate the mean mark of the students, and the standard deviation of the results. [3]

Paper 2 Q1 — Quadratics

> 1) **(i)** Express $x^2 - 7x + 17$ in the form $(x-a)^2 + b$, where a and b are constants.
>
> Hence state the maximum value of $f(x) = \dfrac{1}{x^2 - 7x + 17}$. [2]
>
> **(ii)** Find the possible values of b if the equation $g(x) = 0$ is to have only
>
> one root, where $g(x)$ is given by $g(x) = 3x^2 + bx + 12$. [3]

i | _An easy Completing the Square bit_

'Express $x^2 - 7x + 17$ in the form $(x-a)^2 + b$, where a and b are constants.'

The question's just asking you to _complete the square_. The x² bit's got a coefficient of 1, so it's not so bad...

$$x^2 - 7x + 17$$

Rewrite it as one bracket squared + number.

$$= \left(x - \frac{7}{2}\right)^2 + b$$

> _Don't forget — you just halve the coefficient of x to get the number in the brackets._

> _Have a look at pages 10 and 11 for more on completing the square._

Find b by making the old and new equations equal to each other.

$$x^2 - 7x + 17 = \left(x - \frac{7}{2}\right)^2 + b$$

$$x^2 - 7x + 17 = x^2 - 7x + \frac{49}{4} + b$$

$$b = 17 - \frac{49}{4} = \frac{19}{4}$$

> _Simplify the equation to get the value of b._

$$x^2 - 7x + 17 = \left(x - \frac{7}{2}\right)^2 + \frac{19}{4}$$

Finding the _Maximum..._

'Hence state the maximum value of $f(x) = \dfrac{1}{x^2 - 7x + 17}$.'

It'll be maximum when the quadratic in the denominator is as _small_ as possible.

The minimum value of the denominator is easy to see using your answer to the first part — it's $\frac{19}{4}$, because the squared bit is never less than zero.

> _It says 'hence' — that's a pretty major clue that you've got to use the result from the first part to do this bit._

So... $f(x)_{max} = \dfrac{1}{\left(\frac{19}{4}\right)} = \dfrac{4}{19}$

ii | _Use the Discriminant_

'Find the possible values of b if the equation $g(x) = 0$ is to have only one root, where $g(x) = 3x^2 + bx + 12$.'

You can tell how many roots a function has got if you use the _quadratic formula_. Think about b² – 4ac. If b² – 4ac = 0, then it's only got one root.

> _The b²–4ac bit is called the discriminant — and it's this part that tells you how many roots a quadratic has. See page 9._

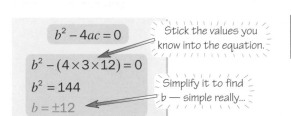

$$b^2 - 4ac = 0$$

$$b^2 - (4 \times 3 \times 12) = 0$$

$$b^2 = 144$$

$$b = \pm 12$$

> _Stick the values you know into the equation._

> _Simplify it to find b — simple really..._

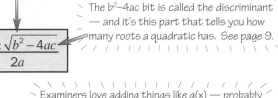

$$x = \frac{-b \pm \sqrt{b^2 - 4ac}}{2a}$$

> _Examiners love adding things like g(x) — probably just to confuse you. They could have just said: 'Find the possible values of b if $3x^2 + bx + 12 = 0$.'_

The square is complete..... Now I am the Master...

One of the commonest completing-the-square mistakes is not noticing when there's a number in front of the x² bit. Either that or noticing it but trying to stick it inside the brackets. Uh-uh. You've got to stick it outside, so it multiplies both the x² and x parts. And with the quadratic formula — you've got to be oh, so careful with those minus signs. So watch it.

Paper 2 Q2 — Differentiation

2 The function $g(x)$ is defined by $g(x) = (x-5)(x-3)(x+7)$.

(i) Show that the rate of change of $g(x)$ with respect to x can be written $g'(x) = 3x^2 - 2x - 41$. [2]

(ii) Hence find the x-coordinates of the stationary points of $g(x)$ to three decimal places. [3]

(iii) Find, to 3dp, the ranges of x for which $g(x)$ is: **(a)** an increasing function of x;   **(b)** a decreasing function of x. [3]

(iv) If $f(x) = x^3 + 3x^2 + kx + 7$, find the possible values of k so that $f(x)$ has no turning points. [3]

---

i | *Simplify it — then Differentiate...*

$$\frac{d}{dx}(x^n) = nx^{n-1}$$

'Show that the rate of change of $g(x)$ with respect to x can be written $g'(x) = 3x^2 - 2x - 41$.'

Not an easy start to the question — but the wording makes it look worse than it is. All it's asking you to do is differentiate the function. (Always differentiate to find the rate of change of something.) And as long as you remember the rules of differentiation, it's not really that bad.

Got total memory loss about everything to do with differentiation? Turn to page 26 for some help.

First rewrite g(x) so that it's in a form you can differentiate (i.e. powers of x).

$$g(x) = (x-5)(x-3)(x+7)$$
$$= (x-5)(x^2 + 4x - 21)$$
$$= x^3 - x^2 - 41x + 105$$

The normal rule for differentiation is...
$$\frac{d}{dx}(x^n) = nx^{n-1}$$

Then using the normal rule for differentiation...

$g'(x) = \dfrac{dg}{dx}$

$$g(x) = x^3 - x^2 - 41x + 105$$
$$g'(x) = 3x^2 - 2x - 41$$

---

ii | *Find Stationary Points by setting the derivative equal to Zero*

'Hence find the x-coordinates of the stationary point of $g(x)$ to three decimal places.'

The question uses the word 'hence', so you know you have to <u>use</u> the part of the question you've already answered.

To find a <u>stationary</u> point, set the derivative equal to <u>zero</u>. Remember — the derivative shows the gradient of the curve, so the curve is flat when the derivative is zero.

You need to solve $g'(x) = 0$

which is... $3x^2 - 2x - 41 = 0$

You found this in the last part of the question.

$$x = \frac{-b \pm \sqrt{b^2 - 4ac}}{2a}$$

The question tells you to give your answer to three decimal places — so that means use the quadratic formula and your calculator (no algebra then — what a shame).

$$x = \frac{-b \pm \sqrt{b^2 - 4ac}}{2a}$$
$$x = \frac{2 \pm \sqrt{(-2)^2 - 4 \times 3 \times (-41)}}{2 \times 3}$$
$$x = \frac{2 \pm \sqrt{496}}{6}$$

$3x^2 - 2x - 41 = 0$, so $a = 3$, $b = -2$, and $c = -41$

Work this out on your calculator to get the answers... $x = -3.379$ **or** $x = 4.045$

Paper 2 Q2 — Differentiation

iii | Find what a function is Doing by drawing a Graph

'Find, to 3 d.p., the ranges of x for which $g(x)$ is: (a) an increasing function of x;'

To find where a function is __increasing__, you need to find where the derivative is __positive__.

The derivative is: $g'(x) = 3x^2 - 2x - 41$.

The easiest way to find where this is __positive__ or __negative__ is to draw the graph of $y = g'(x) = 3x^2 - 2x - 41$ *(the derivative):*

It's a u-shaped parabola, and you've just found where this crosses the x-axis — at $x = -3.379$ and $x = 4.045$.

You know it's u-shaped because the coefficient of x^2 is positive.

From the graph, you can see that $y = 3x^2 - 2x - 41$ (and therefore $g'(x)$) is positive for $x < -3.379$ and $x > 4.045$.

And so the function is increasing for $x < -3.379$ and $x > 4.045$

Remember — this is a graph of $y = g'(x)$, not $y = g(x)$.

'(b) a decreasing function of x.'

If a function's increasing where the derivative is positive, it must be __decreasing__ when the derivative's __negative__.

Using the same graph, you can see that $3x^2 - 2x - 41$ ($g'(x)$) is negative when x is between -3.379 and 4.045.

So the function is decreasing for $-3.379 < x < 4.045$

iv | If f(x) has no Stationary Points, then f'(x) Cannot equal Zero

'If $f(x) = x^3 + 3x^2 + kx + 7$, find the possible values of k so that $f(x)$ has no turning points.'

Nearly there, don't let it beat you now... It's a question about __turning points__, so you're going to have to differentiate. You know that stationary points only occur when the derivative (gradient) is zero, so you'll have to make sure the derivative can __never__ be equal to __zero__.

It's easy enough to differentiate — just use the normal rules...

$$f(x) = x^3 + 3x^2 + kx + 7$$
$$\Rightarrow f'(x) = 3x^2 + 6x + k$$

And now it should all start to make sense — this derivative's a __quadratic__. You've got to make sure it's never 0. This is where the 'discriminant' (that's the '$b^2 - 4ac$' thing) comes in dead handy.

Want to know why this works...? Have a look at page 9.

For a quadratic to have no roots, you need: $b^2 - 4ac < 0$

Here, $a = 3$, $b = 6$ and $c = k$. So you need:

$$6^2 - (4 \times 3 \times k) < 0$$
$$\Rightarrow 36 - 12k < 0$$
$$\Rightarrow 36 < 12k$$
$$\Rightarrow k > 3$$

And so f(x) will have no turning points as long as $k > 3$.

Reason number 10 — maths won't ever dump you...

his looks like quite a tricky question. Not only is the equation complicated, but it's pretty difficult to work out what the xaminer actually wants you to do. But really, this question is loads of simple stuff, all bunged together, a bit like making read. Well... not at all like making bread really... nothing like it... I'm just... ooh.. er.. you still there?.. Taxi...

Paper 2 Q3 — Frequency Tables and Histograms

3 A worker in a duck sanctuary measured the weights of the sanctuary's adult ducks. The following data was collected:

Weight in grams	<1000	1000-1200	1200-1400	1400-1500	1500-1600	1600-1800	1800-2000	2000-2500	2500-3000
Frequency	2	5	5	8	13	18	8	3	1

(a) (i) Calculate suitable frequency densities and, on graph paper, construct a histogram of the data. [3]

(ii) Calculate estimates of the mean and variance of the weights of the ducks. [3]

(b) (i) Represent this information using a cumulative percentage frequency diagram. [3]

(ii) Estimate the median, lower quartile and upper quartile weights of the ducks. [2]

(iii) Use your estimates to draw an approximate box and whisker diagram of the results. [2]

---

a)i | Get the _Frequency Densities_ before you do anything else

'Calculate suitable frequency densities and, on graph paper, construct a histogram of the data.'

To get frequency densities from these frequency tables, find the class width of each frequency band _first_. Then divide the frequency by the class width to get the _frequency density_. It's dead easy.

Take the lower limit from the upper limit to get the class width.

$$1200 - 1000 = 200$$

The lower limit for the first band is 0 (you can't have a negative frequency).

Then divide the frequency by the class width you've just found to get the frequency density.

$$200 \div 2 = 100$$

Do the same for each frequency band then stick them in a table like this...

Weight in grams	<1000	1000-1200	1200-1400	1400-1500	1500-1600	1600-1800	1800-2000	2000-2500	2500-3000
Frequency	2	5	5	8	13	18	8	3	1
Class Width	1000	200	200	100	100	200	200	500	500
Frequency Density	0.002	0.025	0.025	0.08	0.13	0.09	0.04	0.006	0.002

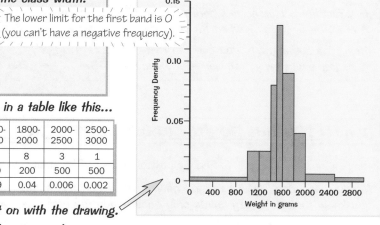

Now the maths is done, you can get on with the drawing.

Plot the histogram with frequency density on the y-axis, and the weight in grams on the x-axis.

---

a)ii | Finding the mean's going to mean (he he) _Loads of Working..._

'Calculate estimates of the mean and variance of the weights of the ducks.'

Finding the mean and variance using frequency tables isn't really much harder than finding it with normal numbers... It's just doing the same kind of thing in a different way. Not convinced? Watch this then...

The estimate of the mean is:

$$\frac{(\text{midpoint}_1 \times \text{frequency}_1 + ...\text{midpoint}_n \times \text{frequency}_n)}{\text{total of frequencies}}$$

While the 'normal' mean-finding method would be:

$$\frac{(\text{value}_1 + ...\text{value}_n)}{\text{total number of values}}$$

So what you're trying to do is say that midpoint × frequency (e.g. 750 × 3 = 2250) is the same as having three identical values (e.g. 750 + 750 + 750 = 2250).

Find the midpoints by adding the upper and lower limits together, and dividing by 2, e.g. $\frac{1200+1000}{2} = 1100$
So the midpoints are 500, 1100, 1300, 1450, 1550, 1700, 1900, 2250, 2750.

Get the mean by multipying each class midpoint by the class frequency. Add all these answers together, and divide the result by the total frequency.

$$(500 \times 2 + 1100 \times 5 + 1300 \times 5 + 1450 \times 8 + 1550 \times 13 + 1700 \times 18 + 1900 \times 8 + 2250 \times 3 + 2750 \times 1) \div 63$$

$$= (1000 + 5500 + 6500 + 11600 + 20150 + 30600 + 15200 + 6750 + 2750) \div 63$$

$$= 100050 \div 63 = 1590 \text{ to 3 s.f.}$$

Practice Exam Two

Paper 2 Q3 — Frequency Tables and Histograms

And now that you've got the mean, finding the variance becomes a whole lot easier.
Again, you've got to pretend that all the data in each class takes the midpoint value.

$$Variance = \frac{1}{n} \sum f_i \left(x_i - \overline{x} \right)^2 = \frac{1}{n} \sum f_i x_i^2 - \overline{x}^2$$

We've used an unrounded figure here. You might lose accuracy if you round down too early.

So, for <u>each</u> class take the mean away from the class midpoint — $1100 - 1588.10 = -488.10$

Square the answer, so you don't have any negatives — $(-488.10)^2 = 238241.61$

And multiply this by the class frequency — $238241.61 \times 5 = 1191208.05$

Then, add all the results together (you should get 3100623.5), and divide by the total frequency (63) to get the <u>variance</u>. — $3100623.5 \div 63 = 4920$ to 3 s.f.

(b) I can't wait — a Cumulative Percentage Frequency Diagram all for me...

'Represent this information using a cumulative percentage frequency diagram.'

The best way to do these is to start with a table. Lean back in your chair, put your feet up on the table, and relax. Maybe make yourself a hot drink, like a nice cup of hot chocolate, with cream... and marshmallows. Mmmm...

Add each class frequency to the previous cumulative frequency to get the new one.

Find the cumulative percentage frequency by dividing the cumulative frequency by the total frequency.

Weight in grams	<1000	1000-1200	1200-1400	1400-1500	1500-1600	1600-1800	1800-2000	2000-2500	2500-3000
Frequency	2	5	5	8	13	18	8	3	1
Cumulative Frequency	2	7	12	20	33	51	59	62	63
Cumulative Percentage Frequency	3.2	11.1	19.0	31.7	52.4	81.0	93.7	98.4	100.0

A Plot a cumulative frequency graph from the table.
Put the classes along the x-axis (weight in grams), and the cumulative percentage frequency along the y-axis.

Plot the points at the <u>midpoints</u> of the class.
Draw a curve through the points as best you can.

Draw horizontal lines from 25%, 50%, and 75% until they meet the curve. Then draw vertical lines at each of those points down to the x-axis.

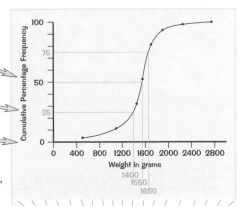

'Estimate the median, lower quartile and upper quartile weights of the ducks.'

B The <u>median</u> is shown by the <u>50%</u> (middle) line — about 1550g.
The <u>upper quartile</u> is shown by the <u>75%</u> line — about 1650g.
The <u>lower quartile</u> is shown by the <u>25%</u> line — about 1400g.

Cumulative frequency graphs are pretty much always this shape. If it looks really different, chances are you've done something wrong.

'Use your estimates to draw an approximate box and whisker diagram of the results.'

C

BOX AND WHISKER DIAGRAMS...

These are dead easy. Draw a vertical line for the median, and the upper and lower quartiles, and then make them into a box, like on the diagram.

Those thin line thingies are the whiskers, by the way.

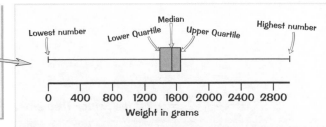

Reason number 11 — if you press the same buttons, you always get the same result...

This is pretty much your typical stats question. That means if you know what you're doing, it'll be easy — though it might take a while. But there's no way you can blag it — it's not like English GCSE where you can write rubbish for an hour, and still get a half decent mark. Not a chance. You've got to know everything here — that means frequency density tables and histograms, how to find the mean and variance, cumulative frequency tables and diagrams (and estimating the median and quartiles from them), and my favourite, box and whisker diagrams (they're fantastic, simply whizzo... oh yes).

Paper 2 Q4 — Algebra

4 (i) Rewrite the following expression in the form $f(x) = 0$, where $f(x)$ is of the form $f(x) = ax^3 + bx^2 + cx + d$.

$$(x-1)(x^2 + x + 1) = 2x^2 - 17$$

[2]

(ii) Show that $(x+2)$ is a factor of $f(x)$.

[2]

(iii) Using your answer to part (iii), factorise $f(x)$ as the product of a linear factor and a quadratic factor.

[3]

(iv) By completing the square, or otherwise, show that $f(x) = 0$ has no other roots.

[2]

_i_ | _Multiply out the Brackets and get everything on one side_

'Rewrite the following expression in the form $f(x) = 0$...'

Looks confusing, but all it's asking you to do is multiply out the brackets and then rearrange it to get <u>zero</u> on one side.

Start by multiplying out the tricky bit:

$$(x-1)(x^2 + x + 1) = x(x^2 + x + 1) - 1(x^2 + x + 1)$$
$$= x^3 + x^2 + x - x^2 - x - 1$$
$$= x^3 - 1$$

Write out the thing you're starting from:

$$(x-1)(x^2 + x + 1) = 2x^2 - 17$$

You've just worked out this bit:

$$\Rightarrow x^3 - 1 = 2x^2 - 17$$
$$\Rightarrow x^3 - 2x^2 + 16 = 0$$

... and take everything over to one side.

This is in the form f(x) = 0, if f(x) is: $\quad f(x) = x^3 - 2x^2 + 16$

$a = 1 \quad b = -2$
$c = 0 \quad d = 16$

... and f(x) is in the form ax³ + bx² + cx + d...

... so your answer is: $\quad x^3 - 2x^2 + 16 = 0$

_ii_ | _Show that something's a Factor — you need the Factor Theorem_

'Show that $(x+2)$ is a factor of $f(x)$.'

**Whenever you see the word 'factor' in a question — think '<u>Factor Theorem</u>'.
There's ALWAYS a question on it. Which is good — cos it's easy.**

See page 14 for more about the Fabulous Factor Theorem.

To show whether (x + 2) is a factor of f(x), find f(–2)...

$$f(x) = x^3 - 2x^2 + 16$$
$$\Rightarrow f(-2) = (-2)^3 - 2 \times (-2)^2 + 16$$
$$= -8 - 8 + 16$$
$$= 0$$

Since f(–2) = 0, by the Factor Theorem, (x + 2) must be a factor of f(x).

THE FACTOR THEOREM (in case you've forgotten it...)

The Factor Theorem says that (x – a) is a factor of a polynomial f(x) if and only if f(a) = 0.

So if you want to show that (x+2) is a factor of f(x), just show that f(–2) = 0.

But don't get the plus and minus signs confused...

To prove that (x+a) is a factor, show f(–a) = 0. To prove that (x–a) is a factor, show f(a) = 0.

Paper 2 Q4 — Algebra

iii | Now you need to Factorise a Cubic

'Using your answer to part (iii), factorise *f(x)* as the product of a linear factor and a quadratic factor.'

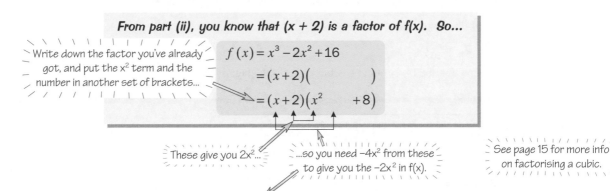

From part (ii), you know that (x + 2) is a factor of f(x). So...

Write down the factor you've already got, and put the x² term and the number in another set of brackets...

$$f(x) = x^3 - 2x^2 + 16$$
$$= (x+2)(\qquad)$$
$$= (x+2)(x^2 \qquad +8)$$

These give you 2x²...

...so you need –4x² from these to give you the –2x² in f(x).

See page 15 for more info on factorising a cubic.

So put the –4x you need in the middle of the quadratic term and you get: $f(x) = (x+2)(x^2 - 4x + 8)$

iv | And for my next trick, I shall Complete the Square...

'By completing the square, or otherwise, show that f(x) = 0 has no other roots, and sketch the graph of f(x).'

Now you've factorised f(x), the next bit's not too bad.

$$f(x) = (x+2)(x^2 - 4x + 8)$$
so $f(x) = 0$ when $(x+2) = 0$ or $(x^2 - 4x + 8) = 0$.

You've already shown that f(x) = 0 when x + 2 = 0.
So, to show that f(x) = 0 doesn't have any <u>other</u> roots,
you need to show that x² – 4x + 8 is <u>never zero</u>.

The question gives you the hint that completing the square will be useful — so try that...

Completing the square with x² – 4x + 8: $x^2 - 4x + 8 = (x-2)^2 + something$
$$= (x-2)^2 + 4$$

(x – 2)² = x² – 4x + 4, so you need an extra four.

Since (x – 2)² can never be less than zero, the smallest value this can take is 4, and so it can definitely never be zero. So that means that <u>f(x)=0 has no other solutions</u>.

Now you've finished the question. You star!

Well actually, I did the question and you just read it. So you're only a little star.

That's you that is.

The question's over — Am I not merciful... AM I NOT MERCIFUL...?

The main thing to take from this page is that the Factor Theorem will definitely be in your exam. I kid you not — it'll be here. And I reckon anyone who knew that would definitely make sure they knew what the Factor Theorem was all about before the exam — especially since it's not even that hard. Think about it — guaranteed marks on a plate. Can't be bad.

Paper 2 Q5 — Application of Calculus

5 A new symmetrical mini-stage is to be built according to the design shown in the diagram.

(i) Find expressions for x and y in terms of r. [2]

(ii) Find, in terms of r and q, expressions for the perimeter P, and the area A, of the stage. [3]

(iii) If the perimeter of the stage is to be 40 metres, show that
A is given by $A = 20r - \frac{r^2}{16}\left(9 + 4\sqrt{2}\right)$. [3]

(iv) By finding $\frac{dA}{dr}$ show that the maximum possible area of the stage is $A_{\max} = \frac{1600}{9 + 4\sqrt{2}}$. [3]

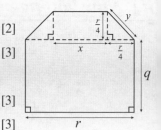

---

i | *Easy stuff with Right-Angled triangles*

'Find expressions for x and y in terms of r.'

It's easier if you just look at the bit of the thing you're interested in.

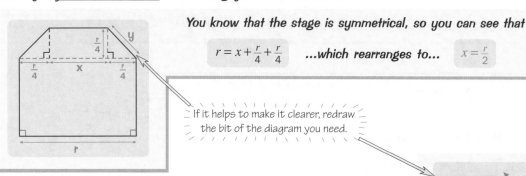

You know that the stage is symmetrical, so you can see that

$$r = x + \frac{r}{4} + \frac{r}{4} \quad \text{...which rearranges to...} \quad x = \frac{r}{2}$$

If it helps to make it clearer, redraw the bit of the diagram you need.

And using Pythagoras' theorem on the top right triangle, you can show:

<u>Pythagoras' Theorem:</u>
The square of the longest side equals the squares of the other two sides added together.

$$y^2 = \left(\frac{r}{4}\right)^2 + \left(\frac{r}{4}\right)^2$$

$$\Rightarrow y^2 = 2\left(\frac{r^2}{16}\right) = \frac{r^2}{8}$$

$$\Rightarrow y = \sqrt{\frac{r^2}{8}} = \frac{r}{\sqrt{8}} = \frac{r}{2\sqrt{2}}$$

$\sqrt{\frac{a}{b}} = \frac{\sqrt{a}}{\sqrt{b}}$

(See page 2 for more about surds.)

$\sqrt{8} = \sqrt{4 \times 2} = \sqrt{4} \times \sqrt{2} = 2\sqrt{2}$

---

ii | *Find the Area and Perimeter*

'Find, in terms of r and q, expressions for the perimeter P, and the area A, of the stage.'

Again, it'll probably help if you draw a picture so you can get a better idea of what's going on.
Do the perimeter first — it's usually easier:

First, write down the total of all the bits: $P = x + 2y + r + 2q$

You already know x and y in terms of r — so use them to simplify this.

So the total <u>perimeter</u> P is: $P = \frac{r}{2} + \frac{r}{\sqrt{2}} + r + 2q$

$y = \frac{r}{2\sqrt{2}}$, so $2y = \frac{r}{\sqrt{2}}$

$$= r\left(\frac{1}{2} + \frac{1}{\sqrt{2}} + 1\right) + 2q$$

$$= r\left(\frac{3}{2} + \frac{1}{\sqrt{2}}\right) + 2q$$

This is in terms of r and q, like the question asks for.

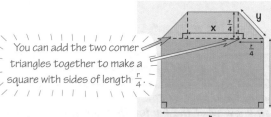

Work out the <u>area</u> from the area of two rectangles and a square.

You can add the two corner triangles together to make a square with sides of length $\frac{r}{4}$.

It's given by: $A = rq + \left(\frac{r}{4}\right)^2 + \left(x \times \frac{r}{4}\right) = rq + \frac{r^2}{16} + \left(\frac{r}{2} \times \frac{r}{4}\right)$

Since $x = \frac{r}{2}$

$$= rq + \frac{r^2}{16} + \frac{r^2}{8}$$

This is the area of the square made by adding the two corner triangles together.

$$= rq + \frac{3r^2}{16}$$

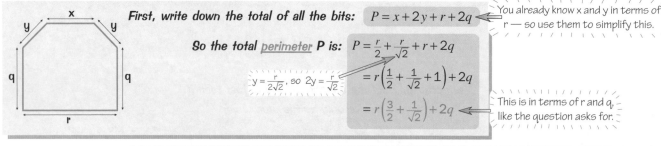

Paper 2 Q5 — Application of Calculus

iii | Put in the Value for A — then Fiddle About a bit

'If the perimeter of the stage is to be 40 metres, show that A is given by $A = 20r - \frac{r^2}{16}\left(15 + 4\sqrt{2}\right)$.'

The question gives you a value for P, so stick that in your equation for the perimeter.

A *Substitute for P in the perimeter equation, and then rearrange to get q in terms of r...*

$$P = 40 \Longrightarrow 40 = r\left(\frac{3}{2} + \frac{1}{\sqrt{2}}\right) + 2q$$

You could rearrange this to get q in terms of r, or r in terms of q. But you need to substitute for q in the equation for A.

$$\Rightarrow 2q = 40 - r\left(\frac{3}{2} + \frac{1}{\sqrt{2}}\right)$$

$$\Rightarrow q = 20 - r\left(\frac{3}{4} + \frac{1}{2\sqrt{2}}\right)$$

B *And then substitute q into the equation for the area.*

$$A = rq + \frac{3r^2}{16}$$

$$= r\left\{20 - r\left(\frac{3}{4} + \frac{1}{2\sqrt{2}}\right)\right\} + \frac{3r^2}{16}$$

$$= 20r - r^2\left(\frac{3}{4} + \frac{1}{2\sqrt{2}} - \frac{3}{16}\right)$$

Watch for sign changes if you take something negative out as a common factor.

C *Rearranging the equation for the area gives you:*

$$A = 20r - r^2\left(\frac{3}{4} + \frac{1}{2\sqrt{2}} - \frac{3}{16}\right)$$

Put all this over the common denominator $16\sqrt{2}$.

$$= 20r - r^2\left\{\frac{(3\times4\sqrt{2}) + (1\times8) - (3\times\sqrt{2})}{16\sqrt{2}}\right\}$$

$$= 20r - \frac{r^2}{16}\left(\frac{9\sqrt{2} + 8}{\sqrt{2}}\right)$$

$\frac{8}{\sqrt{2}} = \frac{4\times\sqrt{2}\times\sqrt{2}}{\sqrt{2}}$

$$= 20r - \frac{r^2}{16}\left(9 + \frac{8}{\sqrt{2}}\right) \Rightarrow A = 20r - \frac{r^2}{16}\left(9 + 4\sqrt{2}\right)$$

iv | And finally, Maximise a Quadratic

'By finding $\frac{dA}{dr}$ show that the maximum possible area of the stage is $A_{max} = \frac{1600}{9 + 4\sqrt{2}}$.'

'By finding $\frac{dA}{dr}$' — that's a hint if ever I saw one. That's the gradient — and you know that when the gradient is zero, it's a stationary point (come on... you DO know that...).

From part (iii) you know that: $A = 20r - \frac{r^2}{16}\left(9 + 4\sqrt{2}\right)$

Differentiating gives you: $\frac{dA}{dr} = 20 - \frac{r}{8}\left(9 + 4\sqrt{2}\right)$

When you differentiate this, you get $\frac{dA}{dr}$ (not $\frac{dy}{dx}$), since you've got a formula for A and you're differentiating with respect to r.

Now A is a maximum when $\frac{dA}{dr} = 0$, and this is when:

$$20 - \frac{r}{8}\left(9 + 4\sqrt{2}\right) = 0$$

$$\Rightarrow r = \frac{8 \times 20}{9 + 4\sqrt{2}} = \frac{160}{9 + 4\sqrt{2}}$$

Don't stop here — this is just the value of r that maximises A. You need the actual maximum value of A.

So put this value of r back into the expression for A to find that the maximum value of A is:

Put your value of r into the equation for A,....

$$A_{max} = 20 \times \left(\frac{160}{9 + 4\sqrt{2}}\right) - \frac{1}{16}\left(\frac{160}{9 + 4\sqrt{2}}\right)^2\left(9 + 4\sqrt{2}\right)$$

...play about very carefully,...

$$= \left(\frac{3200}{9 + 4\sqrt{2}}\right) - \frac{1}{16} \cdot \frac{160^2 \cdot (9 + 4\sqrt{2})}{(9 + 4\sqrt{2})^2}$$

Cancel a $9 + 4\sqrt{2}$ from the top and bottom lines.

...and all this mess should suddenly begin to look more friendly.

$$= \left(\frac{3200}{9 + 4\sqrt{2}}\right) - \left(\frac{1600}{9 + 4\sqrt{2}}\right) = \frac{1600}{9 + 4\sqrt{2}}$$

There. That wasn't so bad, was it? Was it? Hello? Hello? Hellooo... Doctor! Somebody call a doctor...

Differentiate — and the world differentiates with you...

at's often the way with these longer questions — they try to guide you through what you're supposed to do, and one big, fficult question becomes a few smaller, easier questionettes. So don't panic if the question looks impossible when you first e it — it's probably not so bad when you get down to it. And if it's still bad when you get down to it, use the Force...

Paper 2 Q6 — Probability and Diagrams

6   In a multiple-choice exam, where each question has five alternative answers, only one being correct, it is estimated that 75% of all students will know the answer to the first question. If a student definitely knows the answer to the question, it has been found that the probability of that student making a mistake and recording the wrong answer is 0.02. If a student doesn't know the answer, he or she will guess the answer, with a one in five chance of success.

(a)(i) If an answer paper is selected at random, what is the probability that the answer to the first question is correct?   [2]

(ii) If a random answer paper is checked and is found to have the correct answer to the first question, what is the probability that the student actually knew which answer was correct and didn't have to guess?   [2]

(iii) Are the events 'student knows the answer' and 'student gets question correct' independent? Explain your answer mathematically.   [2]

For one particular class of fifteen students, the marks in the test were as shown below:
    53, 47, 94, 84, 78, 63, 91, 45, 66, 66, 59, 62, 51, 68, 72

(b)(i) Draw an appropriate stem and leaf diagram to illustrate these results.   [2]

(ii) State the range of the data, and calculate the mean mark of the students, and the standard deviation of the results.   [3]

This is a probability question. The best way to answer it is to start by drawing a tree diagram, before you do anything else.

TRANSLATION OF PROBABILITY SPEAK

You're told that "it is estimated that 75% of all students will know the answer to the first question". That's an either/or (binary) thing, so it also means that 25% of students won't know the answer to the first question. Obviously...

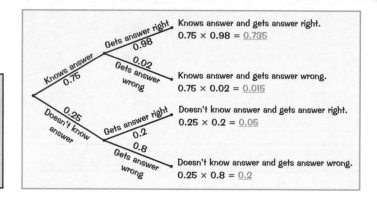

Knows answer and gets answer right.
$0.75 \times 0.98 = \underline{0.735}$

Knows answer and gets answer wrong.
$0.75 \times 0.02 = \underline{0.015}$

Doesn't know answer and gets answer right.
$0.25 \times 0.2 = \underline{0.05}$

Doesn't know answer and gets answer wrong.
$0.25 \times 0.8 = \underline{0.2}$

---

a) i   Easy at first — that's what I like to see

The first part of a question is often really easy — like this bit. It gives you a gentle introduction to the wonderful world of probability, so you don't run out of the exam room screaming, "I can't take it anymore. Help me Mother... help..."

'If an answer paper is selected at random, what is the probability that the answer to the first question is correct?'

> **PIECE OF CAKE**   Add up all the outcomes with the correct answer.
>
> $0.735 + 0.05 = 0.785$

That's the question done. Told you it was easy.

You see this cake. That's this question, that is.

---

a) ii   Use the Tree Diagram to work out the answer

'If a random answer paper is checked and is found to have the correct answer to the first question, what is the probability that the student actually knew which answer was correct and didn't have to guess?'

The wording's pretty tricky in this one — it usually is in probability questions. What you've got to do is work out the probability of a correct answer being written by someone who knew the answer (i.e. not a guess).

> *So... the question is: "What's the probability that the student knew the answer, given that the answer's right?"* $P(A \mid B) = \dfrac{P(A \cap B)}{P(B)}$
>
> *Translate this into what you want:*   *... then stick in the numbers:*
>
> $P(\text{Knows answer} \mid \text{Correct answer}) = \dfrac{P(\text{Knows answer} \cap \text{Correct answer})}{P(\text{Correct answer})} = \dfrac{0.735}{0.785} = 0.936$

Read this off the tree diagram — the probability that the student knew the answer, and got it right, i.e. 0.735.

This is just what you worked out in part (i) — i.e. 0.785.

Paper 2 Q6 — Probability and Diagrams

a) iii | There's a Rule for seeing if events are Independent

'Are the events 'student knows the answer' and 'student gets question correct' independent? Explain your answer mathematically.'

Don't bother trying to think about whether events are independent or not. The question asks you to explain your answer 'mathematically' and that means in numbers and symbols and stuff. You need a formula.

$$\text{Events are independent if } P(A|B) = P(A)$$

So... if the probability of A happening given that B has happened is the same as the probability of A just happening anyway, the events are independent (i.e. if B has had no effect on the likelihood of A).

What the question is really asking is:

"Does a student's answer to the first question depend on whether or not the student knows the answer?"

Of course, you know using common sense that they're not independent. But never mind common sense — you've got to explain it mathematically.

Use the formula: $P(\text{Correct answer} \,|\, \text{Knowing the answer}) = 0.735$

~ You found this in ~ $\rightarrow P(\text{Correct answer}) = 0.785$
~ the first question. ~

$0.735 \neq 0.785$ **so they are** not independent.

b) i | A Stem and Leaf diagram — make sure the numbers are in columns

'Draw an appropriate stem and leaf diagram...'

Stem and leaf diagrams are pretty easy, and can be done really quickly once you know what you're doing. But be careful when drawing them — they've got to be neat so the numbers are in columns. That's why stem and leaf diagrams are useful — they quickly give you an idea of the distribution of the data.

LOOK AT THE SPREAD OF NUMBERS | First find the lowest and the highest numbers (they're 45 and 94).

The first class should be 40-49, written as 4, and the last class should be 90-99, written as, guess what... yup, 9.

Draw something like this first. →
The numbers represent the tens.

4	
5	
6	
7	
8	
9	

Then enter the numbers — 5|3 means 53.

4	7 5
5	3 9 1
6	3 6 6 2 8
7	8 2
8	4
9	4 1

b) ii | Mean and Standard Deviation are just Formula Questions

You don't even have to think for this — all you do is put the numbers into a formula, and stick them in the calculator.

'State the range of the data...'

FIND THE RANGE | This is easy — take the smallest number away from the biggest. $94 - 45 = 49$

'... and calculate the mean mark of the students...'

FIND THE MEAN | Work out the total marks divided by the total frequency. $\frac{53+47...+72}{15} = \frac{999}{15} = 66.6$

$$\text{Mean} = \frac{\sum x_i}{n} = \bar{x}$$

$$\text{Standard Deviation} = \sqrt{\frac{\sum(x_i - \bar{x})^2}{n}}$$

'... and the standard deviation of the results.'

FIND THE STANDARD DEVIATION

Find the mean distance from the mean. You know what to do...

$$\sqrt{\frac{(53-66.6)^2 + (47-66.6)^2 ... + (72-66.6)^2}{15}} = 14.56 \text{ to 2 d.p.}$$

~ If you don't know what to ~ do, you'd better take a ~ look at pages 42-46. ~

Probability — probably the worst topic in the world...

Hey dude, don't make it bad. Take a hard sum, and make it better. Remember, to cancel when you can, then you can start, to make it better. Hey dude, don't be afraid, you were made to pass maths A-level. The minute, you calculate the mean, then you begin, to make it better. And anytime you feel the pain, hey dude...

Answers

Section One — Algebra Basics

1) a) x^8 b) a^{15} c) x^6 d) a^8 e) $x^4 y^3 z$ f) $\frac{b^2 c^5}{a}$

2) a) 4 b) 2 c) 8 d) 1 e) 1/7

3) a) $x = \pm\sqrt{5}$ b) $x = -2 \pm \sqrt{3}$

4) a) $2\sqrt{7}$ b) $\frac{\sqrt{5}}{6}$ c) $3\sqrt{2}$ d) $\frac{3}{4}$

5) a) $\frac{8}{\sqrt{2}} = \frac{2 \times 2 \times \sqrt{2} \times \sqrt{2}}{\sqrt{2}} = 4\sqrt{2}$ b) $\frac{\sqrt{2}}{2} = \frac{\sqrt{2}}{(\sqrt{2})^2} = \frac{1}{\sqrt{2}}$

(there are other possible ways to do these questions)

6) $136 + 24\sqrt{21}$

7) a) $\frac{1}{2}(\sqrt{7} - 1)$ b) $1 + \sqrt{3}$ c) $7\sqrt{3}(\sqrt{5} - 2)$

8) a) $\frac{52x + 5y}{60}$ b) $\frac{5x - 2y}{x^2 y^2}$ c) $\frac{x^3 + x^2 - y^2 + xy^2}{x(x^2 - y^2)}$

9) a) $\frac{3a}{2b}$ b) $\frac{2(p^2 + q^2)}{p^2 - q^2}$ c) 🐦 = 🐦🐦

10) Identity symbol is $\equiv$.

11) a) $a^2 - b^2$
b) $a^2 + 2ab + b^2$
c) $25y^2 + 210xy$
d) $-x^2 + 2x$ or $x(2 - x)$
e) $3x^2 + 10xy + 3y^2 + 23y + 13x + 14$

12) a) $2x(x + 2 + 3x^2)$
b) $yz(6x^2 + 2y - 3z)$
c) $8(2y + xy + 7x)$
d) $(x - 2)(x - 3)$

13) a) $(x + 1)^2$ b) $(x - 10)(x - 3)$ c) $(x + 2)(x - 2)$ d) $(3 - x)(x + 1)$
e) $(2x + 1)(x - 4)$ f) $(5x - 3)(x + 2)$

14) a) $(x - 2)(x - 1) = 0$, so $x = 1$ or 2 b) $(x + 4)(x - 3) = 0$, so $x = -4$ or 3
c) $(2 - x)(x + 1) = 0$, so $x = 2$ or -1 d) $(x + 4)(x - 4) = 0$, so $x = 4, -4$
e) $(3x + 2)(x - 7) = 0$, so $x = -2/3$ or 7 f) $(2x + 1)(2x - 1) = 0$, so $x = \pm 1/2$
g) $(2x - 3)(x - 1) = 0$, so $x = 1$ or $3/2$

Section Two — Quadratics

1) a) $x = 1$ or 2 b) $x = -4$ or 3
c) $x = 2$ or -1 d) $x = 4, -4$
e) $x = -2/3$ or 7 f) $x = \pm 1/2$
g) $x = 1$ or $3/2$

2) a) Min is -7 and occurs at $x = 2$ b) Max is 21/4 and occurs at $x = -3/2$
c) Min is -13 and occurs at $x = 1$ d) Min is -1 and occurs at $x = 7/2$

3) a) $b^2 - 4ac = 16$, so 2 roots b) $b^2 - 4ac = 0$, so 1 root c) $b^2 - 4ac = -8$, so no roots

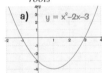
a) $y = x^2 - 2x - 3$

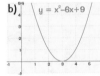
b) $y = x^2 - 6x + 9$

c) $y = 2x^2 + 4x + 3$

4) a) $x = \frac{7 \pm \sqrt{13}}{6} = 1.77, 0.57$

b) $x = \frac{6 \pm \sqrt{52}}{4} = 3.30, -0.30$

c) $x = \frac{-4 \pm \sqrt{40}}{2} = 1.16, -5.16$

5) a) $(x^2 - 16)(x^2 - 1) = 0$ b) $\left(x^{\frac{2}{3}} - 1\right)\left(x^{\frac{2}{3}} - 4\right) = 0$
$\Rightarrow x = \pm 4, \pm 1$ $\Rightarrow x^{\frac{2}{3}} = 1, 4 \Rightarrow x = 1^{\frac{3}{2}}, 4^{\frac{3}{2}}$
$\Rightarrow x = \pm 1, \pm 8$

6) $k > 4$ or $k < -4$

7) Put $x = -2$. $x^3 + 5x^2 + 2x - 8 = -8 + 20 - 4 - 8 = 0$
So by the Factor Theorem, $(x + 2)$ is a factor.

8) a) $(3x - 1)$ Put $x = \frac{1}{3}$ $\Rightarrow 3x^3 + 23x^2 + 37x - 15$
$= \frac{3}{27} + \frac{23}{9} + \frac{37}{3} - 15$
$= \frac{135}{9} - 15 = 0$

so by the Factor Theorem, $\left(x - \frac{1}{3}\right)$ is a factor and $(3x - 1)$ must also be a facto

b) Put $x = -2$. $x^3 + 5x^2 + 2x - 8 = -8 + 20 - 4 - 8 = 0$
So by the Factor Theorem, $(x + 2)$ is a factor.

Section Three — Simult Eqns, Inequalities and Geometry

1) a) $(-3, -4)$ b) $\left(-\frac{1}{6}, -\frac{5}{12}\right)$

2) a) The lines meet at the points $(2, -6)$ and $(7, 4)$.
b) The line is a tangent to the parabola at the point $(2, 26)$.
c) The equations have no solution and so the line and the curve never meet.

3) (i) $x > 5/2$ (ii) $x > -4$ (iii) $x \leq -3$

4) (i) $x \leq -3$ and $x \geq 1$ (ii) $x < -1/2$ and $x > 1$ (iii) $-3 < x < 2$

5) a) (i) $y + 1 = 3(x - 2)$ (ii) $y = 3x - 7$ (iii) $3x - y - 7 = 0$
b) (i) $y + \frac{1}{3} = \frac{1}{5}x$ (ii) $y = \frac{1}{5}x - \frac{1}{3}$ (iii) $3x - 15y - 5 = 0$

6) a) $\left(-\frac{1}{2}, 1\right)$ b) $\left(6, \frac{15}{2}\right)$ c) $\left(\frac{199}{2}, \frac{17}{2}\right)$

7) a) $\left(\frac{1}{4}, -\frac{13}{4}\right)$ b) $(4, 5)$ c) $(-5, -2)$

8) a) $y = \frac{3}{2}x - 4$ b) $y = -\frac{1}{2}x + 4$

9) D is the point $\left(\frac{7}{2}, 7\right)$. So the line passing through AD is
$y = \frac{6}{5}x + \frac{14}{5} = \frac{1}{5}(6x + 14)$.

10) The midpoint of RS is $\left(5, \frac{13}{2}\right)$. The equation of the required line is
$y = \frac{8}{7}x + \frac{11}{14}$.

11) $y = mx$ (assuming it is a straight line)

Section Four — Calculus

1) $\frac{d}{dx}(x^n) = nx^{n-1}$

2) a) $\frac{dy}{dx} = 2x$, 2 b) $\frac{dy}{dx} = 4x^3 + 5$, 9 c) $\frac{dy}{dx} = 15(x^2 + 1)$, 30

3) They're the same.

4) a) $\frac{dy}{dx} = 12x - 6$, so function is increasing when $x > 0.5$, and decreasing whe
$x < 0.5$.
b) $\frac{dy}{dx} = -2x + 3$, so function is increasing when $x < 3/2$,
and decreasing when $x > 3/2$.

5) A point where $\frac{dy}{dx} = 0$. $y = x^3 - 9x^2 + 8x \Rightarrow \frac{dy}{dx} = 3x^2 - 18x + 8$, so
stationary points are at $x = 5.52$ and $x = 0.483$.

6) Work out $\frac{dy}{dx}$ just either side of the turning point.
If it goes from +ve to −ve, it's a maximum, if it goes from −ve to +ve it's a minimum.

7) Stationary points are $(1, -2)$ (Minimum) and $(-1, 2)$ (Maximum).

8) For both curves, when $x = 4$, $y = 2$, so they meet at $(4, 2)$. Differentiating gi
$\frac{dy}{dx} = x^2 - 4x - 4$, which at $x = 4$ is equal to -4. Differentiating gives
$\frac{dy}{dx} = \frac{x}{16}$, and so the gradient at $x = 4$ is 1/4.
If you multiply these two gradients together you get -1, so the two curves
perpendicular at $x = 4$.

9) i) Increase the power of x by 1, ii) divide by the new power, iii) add a
constant. (Or subtitute in limits and subtract for a definite integral)

10) An integral without limits to integrate between. Because there's more tha
one right answer.

11) Differentiate your answer, and if you get back the function you integrated
the first place, your answer's right.

Answers

12) a) $2x^5 + C$ b) $\frac{3x^2}{2} + \frac{5x^3}{3} - \frac{11}{4}C$ c) $\frac{3}{4}x^4 + \frac{2}{3}x^3 + C$

13) Integrating gives $y = 3x^2 - 7x + C$; then substitute x=1 and y=0 to find that $C = 4$. So the equation of the curve is $y = 3x^2 - 7x + 4$.

14) Integrate to get $y = \frac{3x^4}{4} - 2x + C$. Putting x=1 and y=0 gives $C = -\frac{11}{4}$, and so the required curve is $y = \frac{3x^4}{4} + 2x - \frac{11}{4}$. If the curve has to go through (1, 2) instead of (1, 0), substitute the values x=1 and y=2 to find a different value for C, call this value C_1. Making these substitutions gives $C_1 = -\frac{3}{4}$, and the equation of the new curve is $y = \frac{3x^4}{4} + 2x - \frac{3}{4}$.

15) Check whether there are limits to integrate between. If there are, then it's a definite integral; if not, it's an indefinite integral.

16) The area between the curve y = f(x) and the x-axis, between x = a and x = b.

17) a) $\int_{-3}^{3}(9-x^2)dx = \left[9x - \frac{x^3}{3}\right]_{-3}^{3} = 18 - (-18) = 36$

b) $\int_{1}^{9}\frac{3+x}{4}dx = \left[\frac{3}{4}x + \frac{x^2}{8}\right]_{1}^{9} = 16$

a) $y = 9 - x^2$

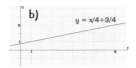
b) $y = x/4 + 3/4$

18) a) $\int_{0}^{1}(4x^3 + 3x^2 + 2x + 1)dx$
$= \left[x^4 + x^3 + x^2 + x\right]_{0}^{1}$
$= 4 - 0 = 4$

b) $\int_{1}^{2}(10x^5 + 8x^2)dx = \left[\frac{10x^6}{6} + \frac{8x^3}{3}\right]_{1}^{2}$
$= \left(\frac{320}{3} + \frac{64}{3}\right) - \left(\frac{5}{3} + \frac{8}{3}\right) = \frac{371}{3}$

19) a) $A = \int_{2}^{3}(x^3 - 5x^2 + 6x)dx$
$= \left[\frac{x^4}{4} - \frac{5}{3}x^3 + 3x^2\right]_{2}^{3} = -\frac{5}{12}$

b) $A = \int_{0}^{2}2x^2dx + \int_{2}^{6}(12-2x)dx$
$= \left[\frac{2}{3}x^3\right]_{0}^{2} + \left[12x - x^2\right]_{2}^{6}$
$= \frac{16}{3} + 16 = \frac{64}{3}$

c) $A = \int_{1}^{3}(x^2 - 4x + 7)dx$
$= \left[\frac{x^3}{3} - 2x^2 + 7x\right]_{1}^{3}$
$= \frac{20}{3}$ (Note : The line y = 4 is a red herring. Ha ha.)

Section Five — Statistics

1) Each dice has 6 sides so there are $6^2 = 36$ possible outcomes...

a) $\frac{1}{36}$ b) $\frac{4}{36} = \frac{1}{9}$ c) $\frac{5}{36}$ d) $\frac{3}{36} = \frac{1}{12}$ e) 0

2) a) (i) A∩B means A and B.   (ii) A∪B means A or B.

b) (i) $P(A) = \frac{4}{52} = \frac{1}{13}$ (ii) $P(B) = \frac{26}{52} = \frac{1}{2}$

(iii) $P(A \cap B) = \frac{2}{52} = \frac{1}{26}$ (iv) $P(A \cup B) = \frac{28}{52} = \frac{7}{13}$

3) 0.9

4) a) A and C are correct.   b) (i) Yes they are. (ii) Yes it is.

5)
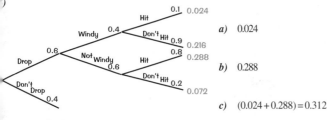

a) 0.024

b) 0.288

c) $(0.024 + 0.288) = 0.312$

---

6) a) $P(A|B) = \frac{P(A \cap B)}{P(B)}$ b) $P(A \cap B) = P(A|B) \times P(B) = 0.8 \times 0.5 = 0.4$
$P(A) = 0.6, P(A|B) = 0.8 \Rightarrow P(A) \neq P(A|B)$
So A and B are NOT independent.

7) If total P(X) = 1, then $p = 1 - (0.4 + 0.3 + 0.2) = 1 - 0.9 = 0.1$

8) $p_2 = \quad P(X=2) = 5k$
$p_4 = \quad P(X=4) = 7k$
$p_6 = \quad P(X=6) = 9k$
$p_8 = \quad P(X=8) = 11k$
$p_{10} = \quad P(X=10) = 13k \Rightarrow \sum p_i = 1 \Rightarrow k = 1/45$

9)

X	1	4	9	16
$P(X = x_i)$	10/27	8/27	8/27	1/27

$E(X) = \sum x_i p_i = \frac{10}{27} + \left(4 \times \frac{8}{27}\right) + \left(9 \times \frac{8}{27}\right) + \frac{16}{27} = \frac{10+32+72+16}{27} = \frac{130}{27}$

$E(X^2) = \sum x_i^2 p_i = \frac{10}{27} + \left(16 \times \frac{8}{27}\right) + \left(81 \times \frac{8}{27}\right) + \frac{256}{27} = \frac{10+128+648+256}{27} = \frac{1042}{27}$

$Var(X) = E(X^2) - [E(X)]^2 = \frac{1042}{27} - \left(\frac{130}{27}\right)^2 = \frac{28134}{729} - \frac{16900}{729} = \frac{11234}{729} = 15.41$

10) a)
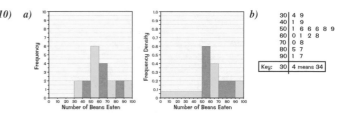
b)

30	4 9	
40	1 9	
50	1 6 6 6 8 9	
60	0 1 2 8	
70	0 8	
80	5 7	
90	1 7	

Key: 30 | 4 means 34

11) mode = 56

median = $\frac{1}{2}(n+1)^{th}$ value = $10\frac{1}{2}^{th}$ value = 59.5

mean = $\frac{1258}{20} = 62.9$

12) a) [cumulative % frequency graph]   b) median = 50mm
upper quartile = 51.5mm
lower quartile = 49.2mm

c) [box plot]

d) IQR = 51.5 – 49.2 = 2.3 mm. 2.3mm < 5 mm and median = 50 mm, so <u>yes</u> — my buns do conform with 9705F.

13) range = 56 – 47 = 9

variance = $\frac{1}{n}\sum x_i^2 - \bar{x}^2 = \frac{51904}{20} - \left(\frac{1018}{20}\right)^2 = \frac{1038080 - 1036324}{400} = \frac{439}{100} = 4.39$

standard deviation = $\sqrt{4.39} = 2.095$

14) a) modal class = 20-30 min.

b) The median is the $\frac{1}{2}(n+1)^{th}$ value.

$\frac{1}{2} \times 26 = 13^{th}$ value so in 20-30 class. Total of 8 before, so 5th value of $\frac{10}{9}$ divisions. Median = $20 + (5 \times \frac{10}{9}) = \frac{230}{9} = 25\frac{5}{9}$

c) mean = $\bar{x} = \frac{\sum f_i x_i}{\sum f_i} = \frac{(3 \cdot 5 + 5 \cdot 15 + 9 \cdot 25 + 4 \cdot 35 + 3 \cdot 45 + 1 \cdot 55)}{25} = \frac{645}{25} = 25.8$ min

d) $s^2 = \frac{1}{n}\sum f_i x_i^2 - \bar{x}^2 = \frac{(3 \cdot 5^2 + 5 \cdot 15^2 + 9 \cdot 25^2 + 4 \cdot 35^2 + 3 \cdot 45^2 + 1 \cdot 55^2)}{25} - \left(\frac{645}{25}\right)^2$

$= \frac{520625 - 416025}{25^2} = 167.36$

e) standard deviation = $s = \sqrt{167.36} = 12.94$

15) $y = ax_i + b$ where $a = -1, b = 60$

a) mean = 60 - 25.8 = 34.2

b) variance = $a^2 \times s^2 = 1 \times s^2 = s^2 = 167.36$

c) standard deviation = 12.94

Index